W9-BSZ-458

# Manuscripts and Documents

# *Manuscripts and Documents*

## *Their Deterioration and Restoration*

*W. J. Barrow*

UNIVERSITY PRESS OF VIRGINIA

CHARLOTTESVILLE

The University Press of Virginia

Second edition 1972

*Manuscripts and Documents: Their Preservation and Restoration* was first published in 1955 by the University of Virginia Press.

The Foreword, by Frazer G. Poole, is reprinted from *The Encyclopedia of Library and Information Science*, edited by Allen Kent and Harold Lancour (New York and London: Marcel Dekker, 1969), II, 257–70, by courtesy of Marcel Dekker, Inc.

ISBN: 0–8139–0408–0
Library of Congress Catalog Card Number: 72–89855
Printed in the United States of America

# Contents

# Figures and Tables

*Figures*



*Tables*

# Acknowledgments

Without the assistance and encouragement of a number of librarians and archivists, the preparation of this volume would have been very difficult. I am, therefore, indebted to Mr. Verner W. Clapp, assistant librarian of Congress; Mr. Randolph W. Church, Virginia state librarian; Mr. Milton C. Russell, reference librarian of the Virginia State Library; Dr. Ray O. Hummel, Jr., assistant librarian of the Virginia State Library; Mr. William J. Van Schreeven, Virginia state archivist; and Mr. Paul M. Angle, secretary and director of the Chicago Historical Society. Mr. Russell also edited the bibliographies on ink and paper.

I wish to thank Mr. W. H. Smith, chief, Organic Chemistry Section, Division of Chemistry; Dr. Robert B. Hobbs, chief, Paper Section; and Dr. Wilmer Souder, consultant; all of the National Bureau of Standards, for reading those portions of the manuscript that pertain to their particular specialties. Mr. Harold J. Plenderleith, keeper, Research Laboratory, British Museum, has read this manuscript, and his suggestions are appreciated. I am particularly obligated to Mr. Smith for his continued help and encouragement over a period of years in my ink research.

For the translations of essential foreign publications, I am indebted to Dr. W. B. Hackley, Department of Ancient Languages, University of Richmond; Madame Charlotte Neveu, Paris, France; Mr. A. Bousse, Archives Generales du Royaume, Brussels, Belgium; Mrs. Bernard Drell, formerly of the Virginia State Library; Miss Margaret Roy Anderson, Rome, Italy; Dr. Gertrude Richards, Richmond, Virginia, and various members of the staff of the Library of Congress.

I am also grateful to many other individuals and institutions for their interest and cooperation. The principal ones are: Mr. Peter Walne, county archivist, Berkshire Record Office, Reading, England; Mr. S. B. Besse, engineer, Newport News, Virginia; the Virginia State Library; the Library of Congress; the Mariners' Museum; Les Archives Nationales de France; the American Philosophical Society; Alderman Library, University of Virginia; Newport News Shipbuilding and Dry Dock Company; and E. I. du Pont de Nemours and Company.

Finally, I wish to thank my secretaries, Mrs. Beverly F. Sydnor and Miss Sylvia D. Beall, for their assistance and for typing the manuscript.

W. J. Barrow

# Foreword

William James Barrow (1904–1967), American investigator of the causes and remedies of deteriorating book paper, was born in Brunswick County, Virginia, the son of Dr. Bernard Barrow and Sallie Virginia Archer Barrow. He graduated from Randolph-Macon Academy in 1923, and later attended Randolph-Macon College. He became interested in problems of paper deterioration when, in the course of investigating the history of the Barrow family, he saw a number of old books which had been restored, and also noted the fragile and deteriorating condition of many old records. Determined to learn all he could about books and bookmaking, he went to Washington, D.C., where he studied bookbinding in the studio of Miss Marian Lane, a former student of Sangorski and Sutcliffe. During this period he also made frequent visits to the Library of Congress, where he observed document restoration methods, which consisted largely of pasting transparent woven silk on both sides of deteriorating documents.

Moving to Richmond in 1932, he established a document restoration shop in the Virginia State Library building. In 1935 he moved this operation to the Mariners' Museum in Newport News, Virginia, where he remained until 1940. During this period he discovered that almost no reliable information about paper deterioration was available. The usual answer to his question of why a particular eighteenth-century manuscript was brittle and unusable was that it was "old." Having examined many much older volumes which were still in excellent condition, he realized that age was not, in itself, the critical factor in paper deterioration. He also became increasingly skeptical of the usefulness of the silking process, which most restorers claimed would preserve a document indefinitely. When, in the course of his restoration work, he observed many documents which, although preserved by silking, were again deteriorating after only 20 to 25 years, he concluded that very little was actually known about the factors governing the permanence and durability of paper. In 1935, he began a research program into the causes of deteriorating paper.

The concern of others with this same general problem had prompted the U.S. National Bureau of Standards to begin a search for better materials with which to laminate documents. Eventually, the Bureau developed a procedure for applying a thin film of cellulose acetate to deteriorated documents. However, the high cost of the steam-heated hydraulic press required to apply this material led Barrow to design his own equipment. Working in his restoration shop in the Mariners' Museum, he invented the first practical roller-type laminating machine.

The original Barrow laminator was made from a ship's armor plating and the roller bearings from a tail shaft. Essentially the device consisted of two electrically heated, thermostatically controlled metal plates for preheating the materials to be laminated, and two revolving calendar rolls with a pressure range of 300 to 2,000 pounds per square inch. The major advantages of the Barrow design were that no artificial cooling was required, and that the pressure applied by the rollers prevented the entrapment of air between the document and the film. In addition, the Barrow process was substantially less expensive than the older silking process and required significantly less time. The first Barrow laminator was perfected early in 1938, and was thereafter used in the restoration of thousands of documents. It quickly became apparent to Barrow, however, that the procedure of laminating a thin film of cellulose acetate to each side of the document produced a laminate with very low tear resistance and relatively low folding endurance. To overcome this inherent weakness in a document laminated only with cellulose acetate, he developed a method of using a sheet of high-grade, long-fiber tissue paper on the outside of the acetate film. This produced a laminate with considerable resistance to tearing and added greatly to the folding endurance of the document.

Despite his development of a superior process for strengthening manuscripts, he continued his investigations into the basic causes of paper deterioration. High acidity had long been believed to be a major factor in such deterioration, but it was left for Barrow to undertake the first comprehensive analysis of book papers, both old and new, and to demonstrate that, with few exceptions, deteriorated documents were highly acid, with pH values ranging from 3.0 to 5.5, while, conversely, older documents still in good condition were low in acid content or even somewhat alkaline, with pH values of 6.0 or above.

Although he continued these studies of book papers until his death, by 1940 he had become sufficiently convinced of the importance of acid as the primary cause of paper deterioration that he began experiments with procedures for deacidifying documents before laminating them. By the mid-1940s, he had developed a method for treating deteriorating documents by soaking them first in a solution of calcium hydroxide, then in a solution of calcium bicarbonate in order to carbonate the residual hydroxide of the first solution. This process neutralized the acidity and precipitated calcium carbonate onto the paper to act as a buffer against any acid that might later attack the paper.

The Barrow claim that acidity was the basic cause of paper deterioration met with considerable skepticism in some quarters, but as the evidence accumulated it became clearly evident that his analysis was correct. Today, the deacidification of those documents that must be preserved indefinitely is accepted archival procedure in the United States and in many countries abroad.

During the course of his inquiries into the causes of acidity in paper, he found numerous instances in which the writing on old manuscripts had eaten holes through the paper. In some cases so-called "mirror writing" was observed where deterioration had occurred on the backs of adjacent sheets. Upon further investigation, Barrow discovered that the inks used on such manuscripts were of the iron-gall type. When the iron of the copperas (ferrous sulfate) combined with the gallic or tannic acids of the oak galls to form the black compound of such ink, the product was sulfuric acid. Tests of old manuscripts written in iron-gall inks revealed that the uninked margins were nearly always less acid than the inked areas.

From this study of early writing inks, Barrow's studies led to an investigation of early papermaking procedures. He had already noted that most papers produced prior to the middle of the seventeenth century were generally in excellent condition and that exceptions were usually attributable to acid inks or to adverse storage conditions. The heavy increase in the demand for paper which occurred during the latter half of the seventeenth century caused papermakers to use a mixture of old and new rags. This resulted not only in a weaker paper but in a much more absorbent paper, requiring heavier sizing to prevent inks from running. Alum, which had long been used in tanning and as a mordant in dying cloth, now came into use in papermaking as a means of hardening the commonly used gelatin size. Tests conducted by Barrow indicated that papers made after 1668 were considerably more acid than those produced before that date. After 1700, increasing numbers of old and usually discolored rags were used in paper manufacture. In turn, these required the use of bluing to make the old rags appear white. In 1774, the German chemist Scheele discovered chlorine, thus making possible the bleaching of even the dirtiest rags. Unfortunately, the properties of chlorine were not fully known, and its indiscriminate use by papermakers decreased the strength of the already weakened fibers from worn rags, and left acidic chlorides which caused further deterioration.

In about 1830 the alum rosin sizing process was introduced into the United States. Whether aluminum sulfate or potassium aluminum sulfate was used at this time is not known. In either case, a chemical reaction occurred which precipitated insoluble aluminum resinate onto the paper to size the fibers and make them less absorbent to ink. This reaction, however, also produced free sulfuric acid. Barrow's tests of some 240 writing papers made in the period between 1700 and 1900 showed that most had a pH of 5.0 to 4.0. By the middle of the nineteenth century the need for paper-making fibers had grown to the point at which rags could no longer supply the demand, and methods for using wood fibers in papermaking were developed as a result. Wood fibers, however, contain approximately 50% noncellulosic compounds which, if not removed before they are processed into paper, quickly break down into acidic compounds. Thus, unless wood fibers are well purified they provide still another source of acid to further hasten the deterioration of the sheet. Barrow's work demonstrated that the combination of inadequately purified wood fibers and alum rosin sizing produced paper which was not only weak to begin with but which, because of the residual acid and acidic compounds in the sheet, almost literally destroyed itself.

From 1940 to 1957, Barrow's research into the problems of paper deterioration was supported by his own resources. In 1957, the Council on Library Resources awarded a grant to the Virginia State Library for an investigation of the deterioration of modern bookpapers to be directed by Mr. Barrow. With the first grant, two studies were conducted, the results of which were published by the Virginia State Library in 1959, under the title *Deterioration of Book Stock, Causes and Remedies.* The initial research program led Barrow to the conclusion that the chemical wood papers, so commonly used in printing nonfiction books during the first half of the twentieth century, were much too weak and too acid to guarantee a reasonable life in either use or storage. In fact, 97% of the book papers so tested were found to have a life expectancy of fifty years or less.

The object of the second study under the 1957 grant was to determine the stability of modern stock book papers and to develop a procedure which would increase the longevity of existing printed materials. Using an adaptation of the procedures he had developed previously for deacidifying manuscripts, Barrow demonstrated that modern book papers could be adequately deacidified and the rate of deterioration significantly decreased by soaking such papers for approximately 20 hours in a saturated solution of calcium and magnesium bicarbonates.

This confirmation of his earlier conclusions, and the demonstration that it was possible to successfully treat newly manufactured book papers to neutralize acidity and materially prolong the life of such papers, led Barrow to the realization that it should also be possible to produce a new and better book paper with built-in permanence and durability. Again, financial support for his work was supplied by the Council on Library Resources in a grant effective March 1, 1959. The project came to a conclusion in March 1960, and the results were published by the Virginia State Library under the title, *The Manufacture and Testing of Durable Book Papers.*

In order to establish reasonable specifications for a strong book paper, Barrow selected seven books printed between 1534 and 1722, all of which were in excellent condition after several centuries of use. His first investigation had shown that the chemical tests usually applied to paper, such as copper number, water extractables, alkali solubles, and viscosity, gave inconsistent and meaningless results. In consequence, he elected to use only acidity as a chemical test, and folding endurance and tear resistance as physical tests. All three were methods which could be measured under standardized procedures established by The Technical Association of the Pulp and Paper Industry (TAPPI). Equally important, the two physical tests selected seemed to be those which most closely simulated the stresses to which book papers were subjected under conditions of actual use.

During this investigation six experimental and two commercial-type book papers were manufactured by incorporating strong, well-purified chemical wood fibers in the furnish, and by using a size (newly available on the market) compatible with alkalinity. The alkalinity of the finished sheet was further increased by adding calcium carbonate as a filler to serve as a buffer during storage. These were the first of what Barrow designated permanent/durable book papers. Such papers, developed in accordance with the Barrow specifications, were first produced commercially in 1960, and have had growing acceptance since that date. Commercial runs of permanent/durable book papers produced since 1960 have shown an increase in the expected permanence and durability.

The original, "Tentative Specifications for Durable, Non-coated, Chemical Wood Book Papers" are as follows:

Based on 25" × 38" size at 60 lb per ream:

1. The paper must be free of ground wood and unbleached fibers.

2. On the basis of a minimum of 15 test strips, from 15 different sheets selected at random from a ream, initital folding endurance of conditioned strips shall average not less than 300 folds in the weakest direction as measured on the M.I.T. tester at ½ kilogram tension.

3. On the basis of a minimum of 12 test strips (selected as in 2) and tested by 5 tears through 4 strips initial tear resistance of conditioned strips shall average not less than 60 grams in weakest direction as measured on the Elmendorf tester.

4. After artificial aging at 100° C ± 2° the average of strips (selected and tested as in 2 and 3) shall not show less than the following fold and tear for the days of aging indicated:

| *Days* | *Fold* | *Tear* |
|---|---|---|
| 12 | 200 | 53 grams |
| 24 | 140 | 48 grams |
| 36 | 100 | 43 grams |

5. The pH of the paper shall not be less than 6.5 at time of manufacture, and after heat aging (as in 4) for 3 days shall show no sharp decline.
6. Opacity of the paper shall not be less than 90.
7. Procedures for testing shall follow TAPPI unless otherwise indicated.

In the course of these efforts to produce a permanent/durable book paper, it became necessary to develop testing procedures which would measure the longevity of the new paper and thus permit valid comparisons with older book papers. As a basis for such tests, Barrow accepted a theory put forth about the turn of the century and more fully developed later by the National Bureau of Standards: that controlled heat aging of paper at 100°C ± 2° simulates natural aging, and that such artificial aging for 72 hours is equivalent to approximately 25 years of natural aging. During this study Barrow undertook a program of extended aging, using heat treatment for periods up to 48 days—the equivalent of about 400 years.

Earlier work in this field had recorded the data from heat aging in terms of the percentage retention of tear and fold at each point in time. In the course of his accelerated aging experiments, however, it became evident that paper degradation followed a logarithmic pattern, and this fact enabled Barrow and his colleagues to develop a method for plotting and analyzing data of heat-aged paper by which the position and slope of the deterioration curve (regression line) could be determined on either semilogarithmic or linear graph paper. With the use of the least-square method and a surveyor's planimeter, rather than a digital computer or desk calculator, the new graphical procedure was simpler to use and gave quicker results.

Although there was criticism of Barrow's accelerated aging techniques, it was widely accepted as: (1) a definite improvement over previous methods, (2) valuable for estimating the potential longevity of paper (although it was recognized that estimates of potential life might vary by 10 to 20%), and (3) especially helpful in measuring the comparative effects of additives, and so forth, on a particular paper, during heat aging (see Figures 1 and 2).

Barrow's contributions to the preservation of books and documents during the years 1936–1961 were of major significance in the field of document restoration. His convincing demonstrations of the fundamental causes of paper deterioration, and the proof that it was economically feasible to produce permanent/durable book paper from wood fibers,

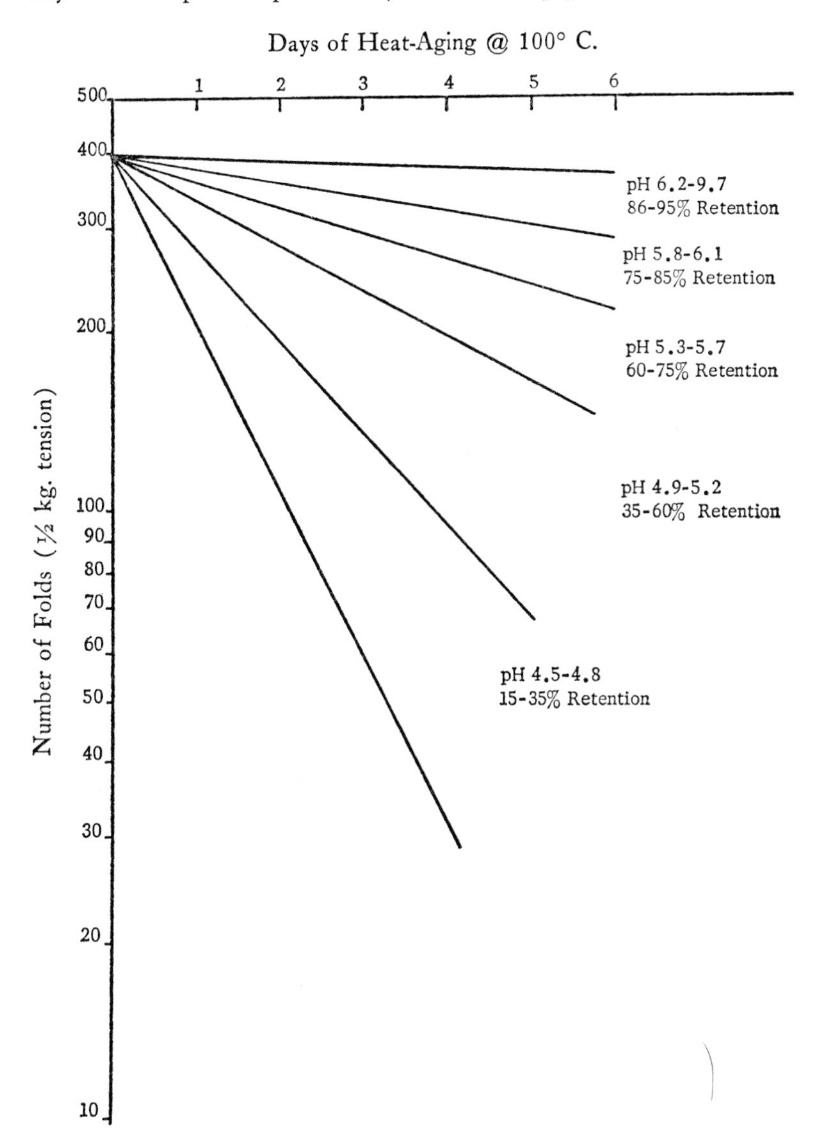


*Figure 1.* Percent retention of folding endurance after 3 days' heat-aging calculated from values on the regression lines formed by heat-aged test data for 41 papers and listed according to their pH range (cold extraction). (Barrow, 1963)

"changed the face of an industry," and provided librarians and archivists with the procedures necessary to preserve their deteriorating collections.

In his investigation of writing inks and their effects upon paper deterioration, he found numerous examples in which the acid in the writing ink had not only eaten holes in the sheet upon which the writing

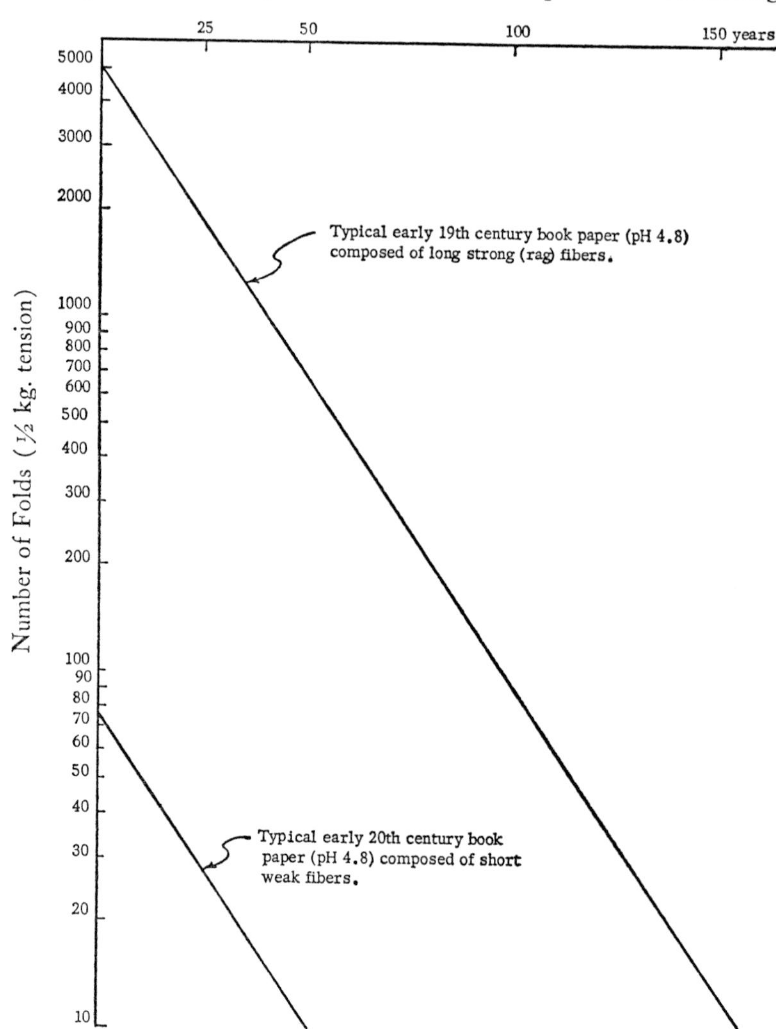


*Figure 2.* Two types of book papers with identical pH and rates of deterioration, but because of difference in initial number of folds it requires 100 years longer for the strong paper to reach the low strength of 10 folds. (Barrow, 1963)

appeared, but had affected adjacent sheets as well. He discovered that documents stored in contact with newsprint (ground wood) had been heavily discolored. Examples of low-grade papers causing such discoloration were observed in the case of file folders, interleaving sheets, end papers, book markers, cover boards, and similar materials. In a study reported in *Archivum*, Vol. III, 1953, he demonstrated that good paper in contact with acid paper is adversely affected by migration of the acid, with resulting loss in the physical strength of the affected document. From this it was a natural step to his recommendation that end papers, file folders, and all other materials used for storing valuable documents, or which might be in contact with such papers, should have a low acid content and should contain no ground wood fibers. Today, storage of manuscripts and documents in acid-free folders is accepted practice.

His investigations of the possibilities of reproducing documents by transfering the ink from a deteriorating page to new and stronger paper led to the development of successful procedures for such transfer. Although the technique was employed occasionally by the Library of Congress and others, it fell into disuse because of the slowness of the process and the competition of cheap methods of reproduction.

In 1961 the Council on Library Resources made its first grant directly to Barrow for the construction of a modern laboratory designed especially for paper testing and equipped with the most modern and precise instrumentation. With these new facilities he continued his studies of the characteristics of book papers and began a fresh series of experiments in paper preservation and related fields.

Among the first projects to be undertaken in the new laboratory, and one of particular interest to librarians, was a research program to develop performance standards for bookbinding conducted for the Library Technology Project of the American Library Association, begun in 1960 and completed in 1965. Barrow and his staff developed standards for bookbindings based upon performance rather than upon materials and methods. The provisional standards developed by the laboratory defined the quality or performance of book bindings used in libraries as affected by three characteristics: openability, workmanship, and durability. This investigation resulted in the development by Robert E. Sayre, a member of the Barrow staff, of the "Universal Book Tester," a machine which made possible for the first time an evaluation of the actual durability of bookbindings by simulating conditions of normal use. A simple but effective device for testing the degree of openability of a book was also developed in the Barrow laboratory in connection with this same program.

An investigation of the permanence and durability of catalog cards was begun by Barrow about the same time, again at the instance of the Library Technology Project of ALA. The results of this study revealed wide variations in the durability and permanence of catalog cards then available. Some 100% rag cards were shown to possess less durability than some 50% rag cards. Strong chemical wood fiber card stocks with a pH of 8.0 or higher showed excellent durability and permanence. Catalog cards of 100% cotton stock with low acid content were show to produce the most durable and most permanent cards. However, card stocks of 100% rag with short, weak fibers and high acid content, proved to be less durable than the strong chemical wood fiber stocks. This program resulted in tentative recommendations for standards for both heavily and moderately used catalog cards. An indirect result was the marketing of catalog cards produced from strong chemical wood fibers in general accordance with the specifications for permanent/durable paper previously developed by Barrow.

In his work on polyvinyl acetate adhesives, Barrow concluded that those which retained their adhesive qualities and flexibility longest, and therefore gave promise of suitability for bindings for the library market, were the internally plasticized copolymers. Two widely used hot-melt adhesives used in adhesive bindings proved to be unstable under heat aging, and were judged unsatisfactory for library bindings since they would not retain their essential charactristics longer than a few months. Mr. Barrow observed, however, in his report on these adhesives, that these results did not necessarily mean that relatively stable hot-melt PVA adhesives could not be made.

Despite the success and wide acceptance of his deacidification process for manuscripts and other unbound materials, it was uneconomical (because of the high labor costs involved in taking books apart, deacidifying the individual sheets, and rebinding) for treating bound materials. With this in mind, one of the early projects undertaken by Barrow after moving into the new laboratory in 1961, was to find a method for treating such materials quicker and at less cost.

When preliminary experiments using ammonia gas as a deacidifying agent proved unsatisfactory, he turned to spray deacidification as a possible solution to the problem. He first tried an aqueous solution of magnesium bicarbonate. This method proved satisfactory as far as neutralizing the acid was concerned, but the cockling effect on paper, and the tendency for an aqueous solution to produce feathering when used on inks or dyes soluble in water created further problems. Dilution of the aqueous solution with ethyl alcohol reduced the cockling effect, but proved to be only a partial answer. Additional work in this field was undertaken by Barrow, but the results have not been published (see Figures 3–6).

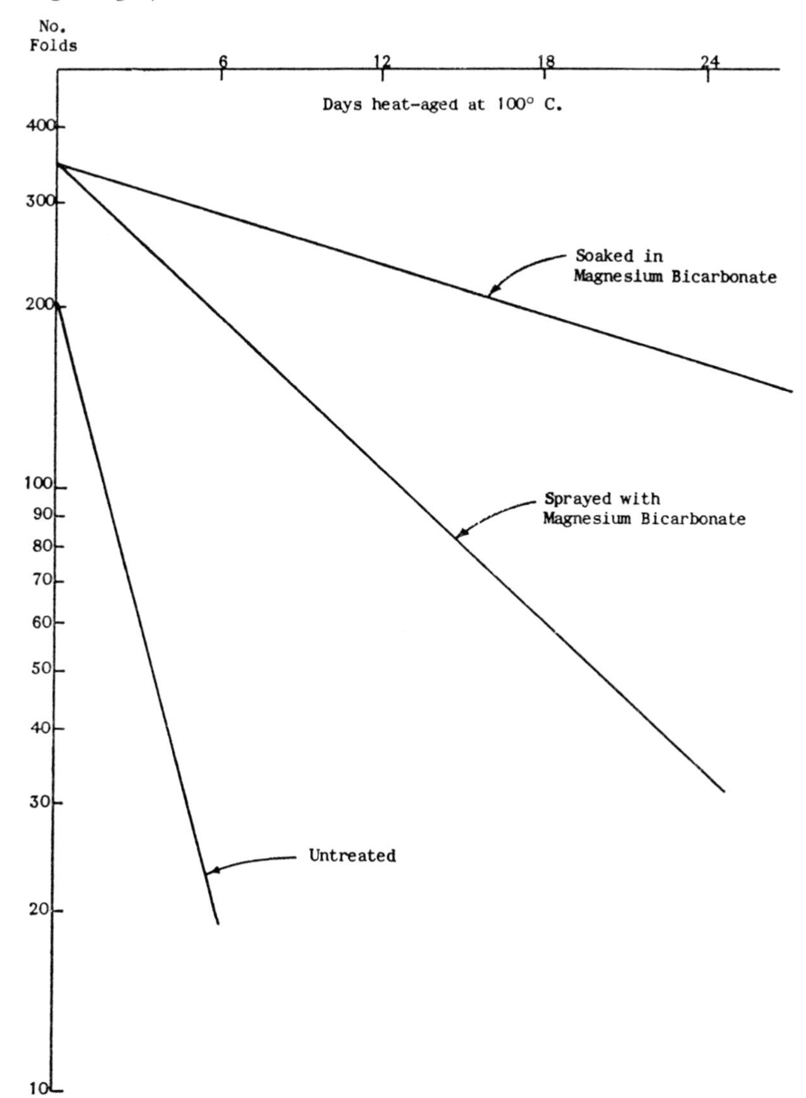


*Figure 3.* The folding endurance regression lines formed from an average of the control and heat-aged data (average both directions) of untreated samples and those sprayed and soaked in a solution of magnesium bicarbonate. (Barrow, 1964a)

Barrow's wide experience with the restoration of manuscripts and other documents and the thousands of tests conducted in his laboratory enabled him to develop a useful categorization of paper as either usable

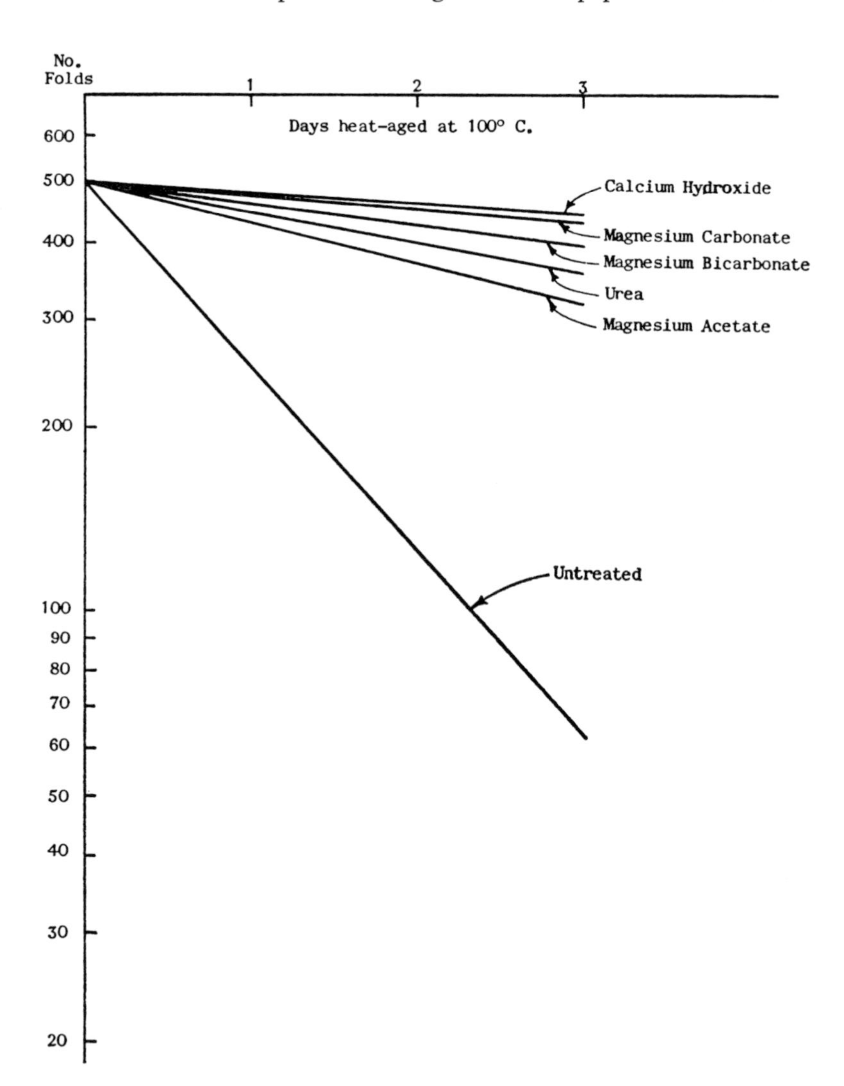


*Figure 4.* The folding endurance regression lines, formed from control and heat-aged data, adjusted at the control to show the rate of deterioration of a modern book paper untreated and after spraying with the indicated solutions. (Barrow, 1964a)

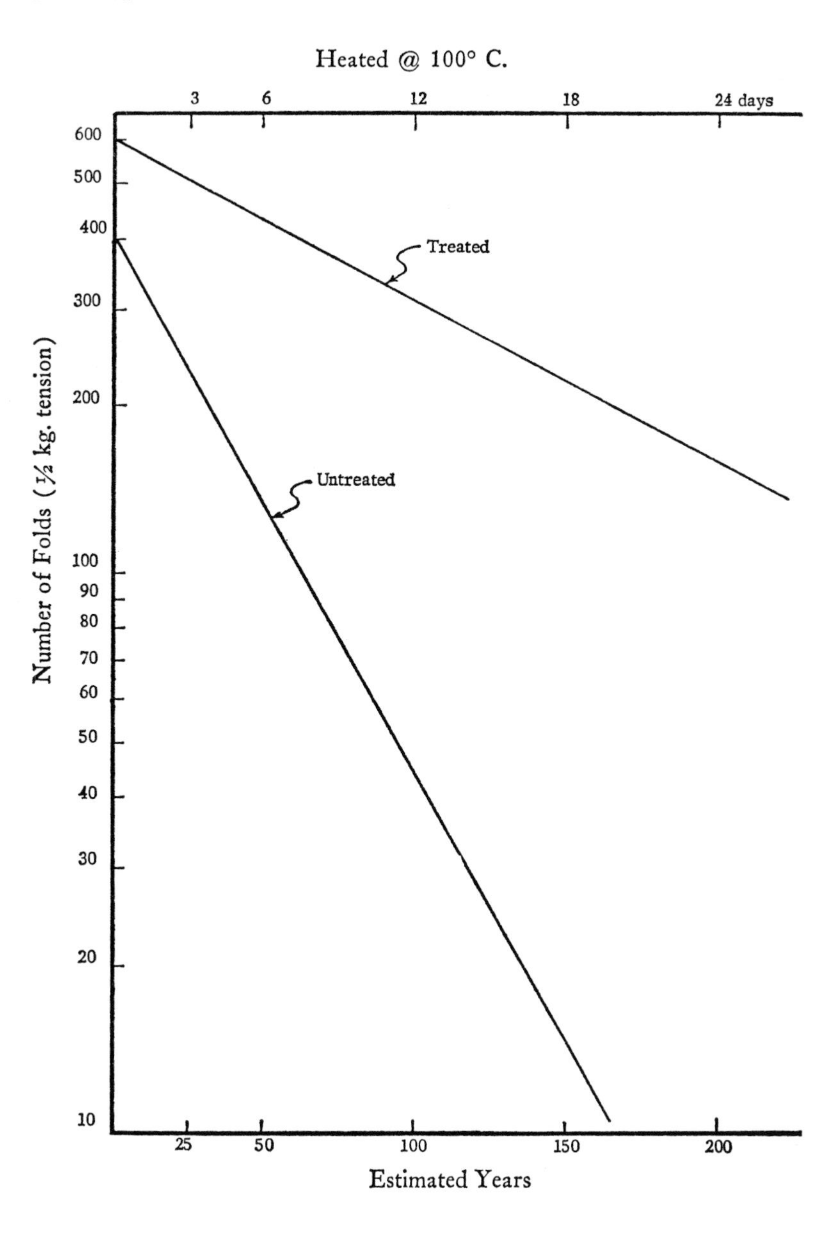


*Figure 5.* The regression lines for folding endurance (M.I.T. ½ kg. tension—average both directions) of 7 book papers (text) before and after spraying with magnesium bicarbonate solution with 25% ethyl alcohol added. (Barrow, 1963)

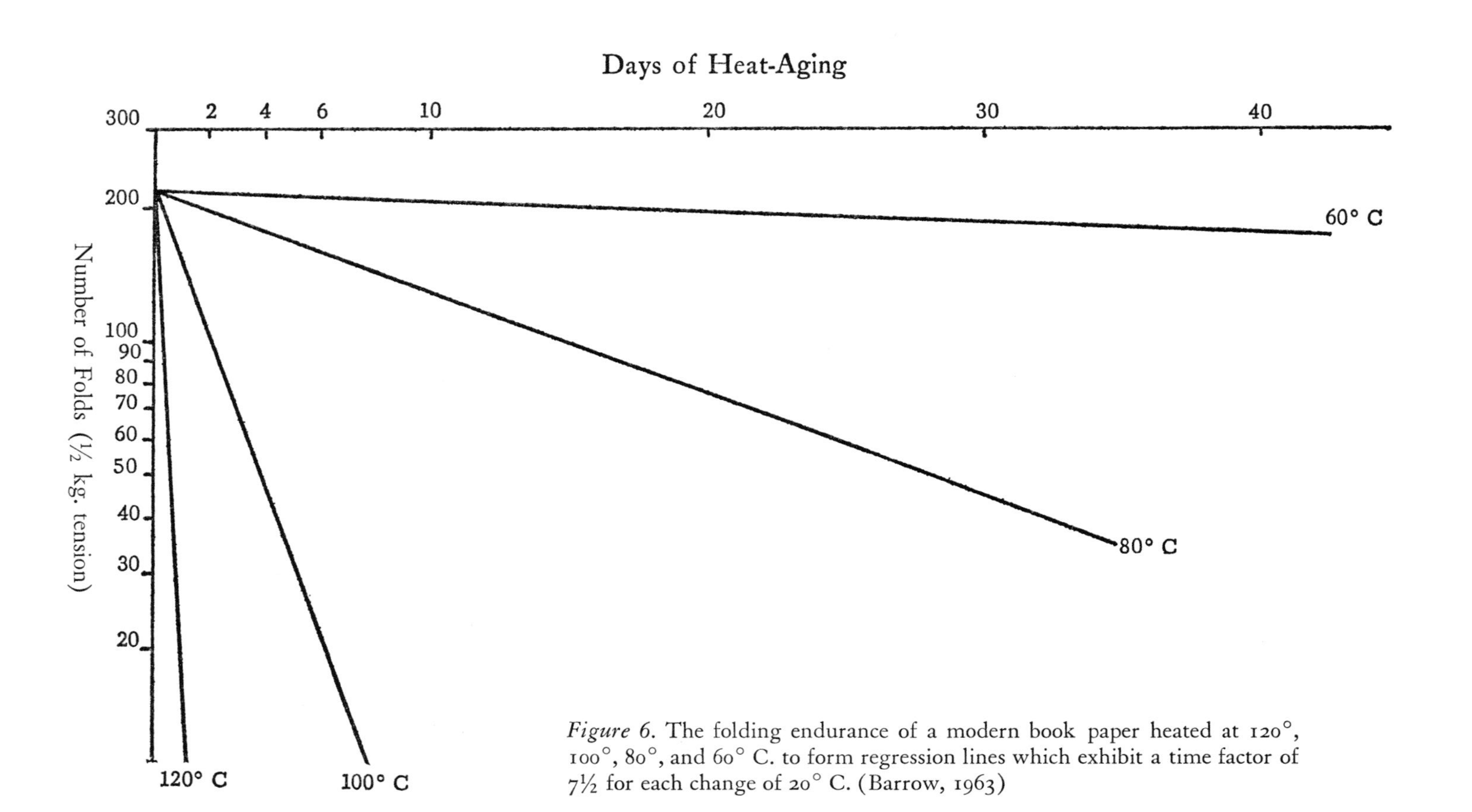


*Figure 6.* The folding endurance of a modern book paper heated at 120°, 100°, 80°, and 60° C. to form regression lines which exhibit a time factor of 7½ for each change of 20° C. (Barrow, 1963)

or unusable. As set forth in *Permanence/Durability of the Book—II*, pp. 41–42, these are as follows:

*High Strength Category*—Has 1000 or more folds and 75 or more grams tear resistance. Because of the filler used to provide opacity, few book papers fall in this category. Many bond and ledger papers composed of strong chemical wood or cotton fibers fall in this category and can be expected to withstand hard usage.

*Moderate Strength Category*—Has 300–1000 folds with 60–75 grams tear. Book papers of this strength have good potential use in the average library. The permanent/durable type book papers fall in either this category or above.

*Low Strength Category*—Has 10–300 folds with 25–60 grams tear or more. These papers have limited potential use and especially those in the 10–50 folds category (newsprint). Many scholarly publications occur in the range of 50–75 folds and will soon need restoration because of the fast rate of deterioration due to high acidity.

*Weak Category*—Has 2–10 folds with 13–23 grams tear. Such a paper is below newsprint strength and should not be subjected to hard use. It is suitable only for a rare book room where users are cautioned to handle it with care.

*Unusable Category*—Has 1.0–0.1 fold with 8–12 grams tear. Such a sheet breaks when creased by the thumb and is difficult to sew if rebound. A leaf in a book of this strength should be turned with much care and is unsuitable for use unless restored.

*Brittle Category*—Has 0.1–0.01 fold with 4–8 grams tear. Crumbles into small and medium size pieces when crushed in the hand. Is unbindable and unusable under normal conditions. Will require a skillful operater to handle without damage during restoration.

*Very Brittle Category*—Has 0.01–0.001 fold with 2.5 to 4 grams tear. Can be reduced to very small particles when rubbed in palm of hand. A skilled restorer of documents should use extra care to prevent damage when applying restoration procedures. The restored sheet should be handled with care to prevent splitting of interior.

*Near Dust Category*—Has 0.001 fold and below with 2.5 grams tear and below. The degree of embrittlement is near that of well-charred paper. Can be deacidified provided tissue is placed on each side before placing between screens and submerging in solution.

A significant aspect of Barrow's research was his conclusion that low temperature increases the longevity of paper just as high temperature decreases it. A preliminary study of one book paper heat-aged at temperatures of 120, 100, 80, and 60°C, indicated that for each drop in temperature of 20°C, it required 7½ times longer to reduce the folding endurance of this paper to a given value. Tests on two additional book papers gave similar results. In consequence of this discovery, he built into his laboratory a series of refrigeration chambers capable of providing complete control of temperature and humidity (see Figure 7).

At the time of his death he was pursuing his investigation of the effect of humidity and temperature on the longevity of paper, in an attempt to identify optimum storage conditions for library collections, and was conducting further research on the effect of alum and alum rosin sizing on the deterioration of book paper.

In addition to the major investigations always underway in his laboratory, Barrow often tackled special problems. Thus, he put his talents to work in an investigation of the sizing to be used in restoring the thousands of volumes damaged in the Florence floods of November 1966. He made two trips to England to assist papermakers there in the production of permanent/durable paper for the *National Union Catalog.*

Barrow was a member of many professional organizations, including the International Council on Archives; the American Society for the Advancement of Science; American Institute of Chemists; Technical Association of the Pulp and Paper Industry; International Centre for the Study of the Preservation and Restoration of Cultural Property, Rome; and the Association for the Preservation of Virginia Antiquities. In 1966 he was awarded an honorary Doctor of Laws by Randolph-Macon College.

The reports he authored or which emanated from his laboratory are listed in the bibliography below.

## Bibliography

Barrow (W. J.) Research Laboratory, *Permanence/Durability of the Book:*

I. *A Two-Year Research Program*, Richmond, Virginia, 1963.

II. *Test Data of Naturally Aged Papers*, Richmond, Virginia, 1964.

III. *Spray Deacidification*, Richmond, Virginia, 1964a.

IV. *Polyvinyl Acetate (PVA) Adhesives for Use in Library Bookbinding,* Richmond, Virginia, 1965.

V. *Strength and Other Characteristics of Book Papers, 1800–1899*, Richmond, Virginia, 1967.

VI. *Spot Testing for Unstable Modern Book and Record Papers*, Richmond, Virginia, 1969.

Barrow, W. J., "Hot vs. Cold Extraction Methods for Making a pH Determination," *Tappi*, 46, 468 (1963a).

Barrow, W. J., *Manuscripts and Documents: Their Deterioration and Restoration.* University of Virginia Press, Charlottesville, 1955.

Barrow, W. J., and R. C. Sproull, "Permanence in Book Papers," *Science* 129, 1075 (April 24, 1959).

Virginia State Library, *Deterioration of Book Stock—Causes and Remedies; Two Studies on the Permanence of Book Paper*, conducted by W. J. Barrow, edited by Randolph W. Church, Richmond, 1959. (*Virginia State Library Publications*, No. 10.)

Virginia State Library, *The Manufacture and Testing of Durable Book Papers. Based on the Investigations of W. J. Barrow*, edited by Randolph W. Church, Richmond, 1960. (*Virginia State Library Publications*, No. 13.)

FRAZER G. POOLE

# Manuscripts and Documents

# I Purpose of This Study

UNTIL the latter part of the nineteenth century, the principal method of preserving the text of a deteriorated document (manuscript or printed material) was to make a transcript or some other type of copy. Since that time, good progress has been made in developing restoration methods, and today repair shops may be found in many large libraries and archives. During the past few decades, the extraordinary increase in the use of historical documents, along with other factors, has created a greater demand and need for restoration than ever before. Adverse storage conditions comprise one of the important agents contributing to the deterioration of documents. Probably the most important, however, has been the gradual lowering in the quality of materials used for writing during the past three hundred years.

These three factors have presented quite a serious problem to the custodian of early records. Modern methods of photoduplication are a great aid in helping to solve this problem in regard to usage, but they are not at all the answer to the preservation of an original document in a deteriorating condition. The document of historical interest will be treasured by the future scholar as much as or even more than by the present generation. It is, therefore, the duty of the custodian to utilize those methods of restoration which, to the best of his knowledge, will preserve deteriorated documents for the maximum number of years. At times, it is a great temptation for the custodian to use processes which are simple and which have a low first cost, even though they may not be necessarily the best. The factors that determine the best procedures are those that promise stability; procedures which are known to cause, or may cause deterioration should be rejected.

During the past few decades, good progress has been made in determining the factors governing permanency or deterioration in documents, but as yet all of them may not be known. Much of the data presented here which substantiates these factors has been assembled from historical treatises, or has been based on laboratory studies. The principal purpose in this publication is to record some of this information and describe the recently developed restorative procedures. Thus, as time passes, the librarian, archivist, and scientist will have a better understanding of modern processes and will be able to make a better evaluation of the procedures and effect improvements.

There will be no attempt to describe these processes in such detail that this publication would serve as a textbook or guide for those engaged in restoration work. While this information may be of value for a background in this field of work, no efforts should be made to restore documents of value without proper instructions or a long period of experimentation. The processes that seem to have good properties will be described at some length, but the older and some later methods will be discussed only to show their particular characteristics. The discussion will be confined to the processes applicable to documents composed of the papers and inks typical of the general period from 1400 to 1850.

No attempt will be made to recommend any procedures of applying materials of reinforcement as a means of preserving documents in good physical condition. In this country, and especially abroad, there may be found many manuscripts written five hundred or more years ago which are in an excellent state of preservation. This confirms the opinion of many chemists and students of preservation that paper properly made and stored will last almost indefinitely. There is good reason to think that most of these papers will last many more centuries. Since this condition exists among papers, then restoration of documents in good condition is quite unnecessary. It is usually considered desirable to retain a document in its original state as far as is possible, and therefore restorative or preservative methods are applied only when there is evidence of deterioration or possible injury by further handling. Of course, if documents in good condition have been subjected to adverse conditions, such as soaking in sea water or storing in very polluted air, then it is desirable to remove any residual compounds that may be injurious to their preservation.

## The Basic Requirements in Restoration Processes

At the present time, many manuscripts and printed books are in need of restoration. Generally, limited means make it necessary that the librarian and archivist select for restoration only materials in current demand, or those which they think will be valued most by future scholars. Any process considered should assure the basic requirements of legibility, permanency, and durability. These qualities are more fully described as follows:

*Legibility.* The restorative procedures and materials should not appreciably reduce legibility or interfere in making photographic reproductions.

*Permanency.* Those impurities within the document that have caused deterioration should either be eliminated or rendered inert. All materials used to strengthen the deteriorated sheet should have high chemical purity and stability, and, if possible, resistance to the harmful action of certain agents under normal storage conditions and usage. The procedures themselves or the addition of chemicals should not have a harmful effect on the permanency of the documents.

*Durability.* All materials used to provide added physical strength should give the maximum tear resistance and folding endurance for documents receiving frequent usage. Exhibit items with high aesthetic value and others that are very seldom used may have this requirement lowered. Methods of storage should be designed to prevent injury or unncessary stresses.

All of the above requirements are needed in a restored document, as any two of them without the third does not produce a product which will give the needed properties for a sheet having frequent use over a period of many years. No one of these requirements should be overemphasized to the extent that the others suffer materially. Past experiences have demonstrated that this has happened in a number of restoration processes and has resulted in considerable disappointment to the custodians.

## Early Methods of Restoration

During the latter part of the nineteenth century, the silk process was developed for the restoration of documents. This process demonstrates what will happen when an unstable material is used for reinforcement. For several years, many books that were silked some sixteen to thirty years previously have been brought to me for rerestoration. In a number of these books which had missing portions in the leaves, the silk had disintegrated and completely disappeared in those areas. This is an example of the old paper helping to preserve the silk rather than the silk preserving the document. There are silks which have lasted many years, but those that are treated to give high transparency seem to have a limited stability. The manufacturers of garments recognize this fact, and, in many instances, they are now using nylon instead of silk. I have examined two lots of this highly transparent silk cloth which had been in storage for approximately fifteen years and it had become yellowed and brittle. More information is needed to determine the properties that govern permanency in silks.

At times, a thin tissue of good stability has been used in the place of silk for restoration. By this procedure, only a limited amount of strength is added to the original sheet unless a tissue of sufficient thickness to impart good strength is used. In the latter case, legibility reaches a very low point. The starch paste used in applying both tissue and silk has a tendency to harden over a period of time, but it is not considered chemically injurious to paper. It does make the document more susceptible to attack by microorganisms and insects, a factor of importance in all climates, and especially in the tropics. Undoubtedly, the large amounts of alum sometimes used in making this paste has accelerated the deterioration of the document, tissue, and most probably the silk. This compound is acidic, and laboratory tests show that it can be tolerated only in very minute quantities in papers which are expected to last.

Two other methods of restoration have been tried, but have failed due to the fact that practically no strength is added to the deteriorated document. One method consists of spraying a plastic film over the surface of the sheet to form a protective coating. This does prevent the absorption of undesirable dust particles and so forth. The earlier sprays, however, were composed of cellulose nitrate which is now considered unstable and injurious to paper. The other process is inlaying the document within another sheet of paper to form a supporting frame. The rate of expansion and contraction due to the change in temperature and humidity is seldom the same in two different papers, thus producing the formation of undesirable cockles and a premature breakdown of the document.

## Impurities in Deteriorated Documents

One of the major objectives in any restorative process was unrecognized when such early procedures as silking were developed. This is the removal of, or the rendering inert of the impurities in the document that have caused deterioration. This is important, *as the document itself is the item which the custodian wishes to preserve*. Most of the components that have caused deterioration are acidic and are still active within the paper fibers.

Many of these compounds are migratory, and until recently it was not realized that they often migrate to adjoining sheets during a long period of storage. Similar conditions have been found in documents restored by the silk and tissue processes. When silk or tissue is removed from sheets needing rerestoration, the silk or tissue is often completely eaten away by the migratory sulfuric acid in an area containing a heavy deposit of iron gall ink. Other examples exhibiting migration are occasionally found in the rerestoration of a book. Since many injurious compounds are migratory, it is logical to suspect that the decomposition of silk can have an adverse effect on the old document.

Since the impurities in deteriorated documents continue to be active and migratory, their removal from the paper before restoration is a necessary procedure. The manufacturer of high-grade papers likewise finds the purification of rags and other materials an indespensible procedure in order to make papers of high permanency. The question arises, what are these compounds, and how did they happen to become a part of the document? This cannot be answered without considering the formulation of ink, papermaking procedures, and the possible compounds absorbed by the document during unfavorable storage conditions. Any one or all of these may contribute to the breakdown of a document. The three chapters that follow, which cover ink making, paper making, and storage conditions, have been incorporated in this publication to give the reader a better knowledge of the possible components of a deteriorated document.

# II Inks

THE writing inks of primary interest in this study are the blacks and the occasionally used reds and blues. The two common black writing fluids were composed of either carbon or iron and galls. The carbon ink was known to the Romans as *atramentum scriptorum*, and sometimes was called simply *atramentum*. It is the earliest known writing fluid. The iron ink was known as *encaustum* during the Middle Ages, later as iron gall ink, and today as gallotannate of iron. Recent investigations have indicated that it was used as early as the time of Christ, but did not come into general use until several centuries later. An examination of the ink formulae and manuscripts of the period 1400 to 1850 indicated that the iron gall ink, or *encaustum*, was used almost exclusively in the Occident.

## Carbon Inks

The carbon inks were composed generally of either soot, lampblack, or some type of charcoal to which were added gum arabic and a solvent such as water, wine, or vinegar. The carbon blacks gave color to the ink and the gum arabic performed the following functions: it emulsified the oils in the blacks, gave vicosity to the fluid, helped to hold the carbon particles in suspension, and formed a binder to hold these particles to the document. This ink was usually kept in a powdered form, and water was added "when there was an occasion to write."

The carbon particles of this ink do not fade over a period of time and are unaffected by light rays and bleaching agents. As a rule, these particles and gum arabic contain no compounds which are considered injurious to paper. These properties are very much valued in inks. However, this ink has two capital imperfections which no doubt account for its limited use. It may smudge during damp weather, and it can be easily washed from the document. These characteristics must have alarmed the ancient and medieval scholars who realized that their manuscripts might, in time, suffer the same fate of earlier ones which were being de-inked to recover material for writing.

This factor may have prompted Pedanius Dioscorides (fl. A.D. 60), a Greek physician, scientist, and writer, or one of his predecessors, to add a little ferrous sulfate to his carbon ink. After a few days, the ferrous sulfate will convert gradually to a basic ferric sulfate and various oxides of iron to form a hard encrustation. This makes the characters more difficult to wash off. The addition of this chemical may account for many of the palimpsests in existence. It is a very soluble compound and would penetrate the fibers of the document to form, in due time, the brown, insoluble compounds mentioned above. When a document written in this type of ink was de-inked by washing, the brown compounds of iron remained on or below the surface of the sheet. Even a scraper, also used to remove writings, was not always fully effective without damaging the writing surface of the sheet.

It is also entirely possible that the ancients may have reasoned that if a little ferrous sulfate made their carbon ink less easily washed from a document, then more would do a better job. With much larger additions of this chemical, brown writing with black particles would result. This undesirable appearance could be corrected easily by the addition of galls, which would produce a mixture of both carbon and iron gall inks. They well understood that a black compound was produced when the extracts of galls, sumac, and so forth were added to either iron or copper sulfates. This principle was used in making hair dyes, blacking for shoes, and other items. More research is needed to substantiate this possible development of iron gall inks. Aurelius Cornelius Celsus (b. circa 25 B.C.), a Roman physician, and other contemporaries of Dioscorides used the *atramenti* to heal cuts and burns in the human body as well as for writing inks. In some of these formulae are found not only carbon and gum arabic, but also ferrous sulfate and galls. The addition of the latter two compounds could have been either to improve the aforementioned ink properties or for purely medicinal reasons.

## Iron Gall Inks

The basic ingredients of *encaustum*, or iron gall inks, are copperas, galls, gum arabic, and a solvent such as water, wine, or vinegar. If compounded with the proper amount of gum arabic, this ink will flow easily from a quill pen and penetrate the fibers of the paper to form a black, insoluble compound. Writings made of these inks are difficult to bleach or remove from the paper without leaving some evidence of alteration. These were qualities highly valued in ink, and were often mentioned in the formulae as the principal reason for their use. The characteristics of this ink along with the nature of paper fibers make the de-inking of manuscripts, as practiced on vellum in the ancient era and the Middle Ages a highly impractical operation. Scholars should be grateful for both the introduction of paper and iron inks, for otherwise many early manuscripts would today be indecipherable palimpsests.

For many centuries, the ingredients of this highly valued ink have been essential in the development of pharmacy, tanning, dyeing, and many other processes. The production of many of these ingredients has changed but little basically during the past several hundred years.

## Copperas

Today, copperas is technically known as ferrous sulfate, but during the period of this study (1400–1850) it was known by many other names, such as green vitriol, sal martis, sulfate of iron, copperas, and often as just vitriol. The ancients usually spoke of it as *chalkanthon*, but it was known also by other names, which no doubt accounts for some of the translators confusing it with copper sulfate. Gaius Plinius Secundus (A.D. 23–79), the famous Roman writer and scientist, recommended a streak test on papyrus which had been dipped previously in gall extract to distinguish these two compounds. The wide variations in the quantities prescribed in medicines also indicated that they well understood the difference.

Dioscorides and Pliny describe two methods of making copperas. One was by exposing certain yellow earths to the action of frost and rain water which was carried off and gradually evaporated. The other was the natural evaporation of water from certain wells in Spain which were known to contain ferrous sulfate. Each of these writers had a high regard for the crystals which were "azure" in color, and formed like a "bunch of grapes." A description of a process used in 1678, and similar to the first process described above, may be found in *Philosophical Transactions of the Royal Society* (XII, 1056). This consisted of oxidation of pyrites on exposure to air, and rain water was allowed to dissolve and carry off into a lead chamber the copperas and sulfuric acid formed in the process. Heating the solution with scrap iron produced a greater yield due to interaction of the iron and sulfuric acid.

Arthur and Charles R. Aikin of London stated in 1807 that the same process was followed in France, but in Germany no scrap iron was used. Since the use of this scrap iron varied from place to place, the amount of residual sulfuric acid in the copperas crystal would also vary. This may account, in some instances, for the high acidity found in some early writings. This, in turn, would cause deterioration in the cellulose fibers of paper.

The Aikins further state that this process had changed little since the reign of Queen Elizabeth. They and others recommended for ink making the use of the clear green crystals of copperas in preference to those containing ochre (basic ferric sulfate), which produces sediment in the ink.

## Galls

Gall is an excrescence produced when the commonly called gall wasp punctures the bark of an oak tree and deposits an egg. When the larva develops, the tree produces the gall, which serves not only as a home but also as food for this insect. If the larva dies or leaves the gall at a certain stage, the tree discontinues the production of tannic and gallic acids within the gall. The highest content of these acids is attained just before the insect leaves its home by boring a hole through the wall of the gall. The extract of these galls contains tannic and gallic acids which combine with the iron in copperas to form the black pigment of iron gall inks.

The unperforated blue or Aleppo gall was the type usually recommended as it has the highest content of gallic and tannic acids. The brown English gall, "vulgarly called oak apples," and those of southern Europe were generally considered inferior to the Aleppo. According to the Aikins, Davy extracted 12.5 percent soluble matter from ordinary galls, and 46 percent from Aleppo, the latter extract containing about 90 percent gallic and tannic acids. Modern methods of extraction by Charles A. Mitchell and Thomas C. Hepworth have shown that the Aleppo contains 52.9 percent to 79.5 percent tannic and 3.2 percent to 11.2 percent gallic acids, while the British gall contains only 3.8 percent to 36.7 percent tannic and 0.0 percent to 1.5 percent gallic acids.

There were various methods used to properly extract the "virtue of the gall." Pietrus Maria Caneparius, a Venetian physician of the sixteenth and seventeenth centuries, recommended that galls be boiled as long as it takes to repeat the Pater Noster three times. In many instances, the formulae called for soaking the galls for four to twelve days in the sun in the summer, or by the fire in winter. Fermentation as well as heat was a factor in this extraction process. William Lewis, mid-eighteenth-century scientist of England, found through experimentation that a greater yield was obtained by reducing the galls to a powder than by the general practice of breaking them into several pieces. He, as well as some of the ancients, was aware that oak bark, sloe bark, sumac, pomegranate peels, and other plants contained these acids, but he was unable to extract them in sufficient concentration for making ink. One of the earliest mentions of galls was by Theophrastus (circa 370–285 B.C.), Greek scientist and author, who describes the different types and mentions their use in tanning and dyeing.

## Gum Arabic

The acacia tree is the source of gum arabic, which according to the Aikins was imported from Egypt and the Levant. In describing this gum, they state that it "oozes" from the tree into round, yellowish-white drops about the size of a partridge egg. In the formulae, it is frequently referred to as gum. Caneparius called it the "tears of Arabia," and states that it gives body to the ink and keeps it from flowing too freely. Lewis attributes the following properties to gum arabic: it gives viscosity or body to make the ink flow well; it prevents the ink from spreading; and it suspends the coloring matter and does not sour easily.

The ancient ink formulae also contained gum arabic which was no doubt used not only to give proper viscosity to the writing fluid, but also in some cases as an adhesive to hold the ink particles to the manuscript. I have experimented with various inks and found that gum arabic is needed in ink when a reed or quill pen is used, but this is not true with the modern steel or fountain pen. Many of the modern ink chemists have not realized that the early chemist had a good understanding of the need of proper viscosity in a writing fluid, and they have in some cases incorrectly concluded that the only use of this gum in iron gall ink was for an adhesive.

## Solvents

Rain water was the solvent most frequently recommended in the formulae for making iron gall ink as it was the purest water generally available. In a few instances, river or spring water was mentioned, but in areas of hard water, additional sedimentation would form in the ink if this water were used. Vinegar was suggested in a few formulae, but its acrid and unpleasant odor probably limited its use. White wine was second in popularity among the solvents. Lewis states that white wine gave a better color to ink when first made, and that this effect was more pronounced with vinegar. A slight increase in solubility of the gallic acid and a somewhat inhibiting effect on mold and bacteria might result due to the alcoholic content of wine. These relatively small virtues seem to lend themselves to forensic disputation. I have tried making ink with French white wine and, in my opinion, the delightful ethereal odor given off by this solvent is probably the principal reason for its frequent use. Since odors affect the brain, it may be appropriate to suggest using vinegar for the solvent when writing to an enemy, and wine when writing to a friend.

## Ink Making

The aforementioned copperas, galls, gum arabic, and solvent were all needed to make an ink suitable for writing on paper with a quill pen. In compounding this ink, generally the galls were first placed in the solvent to extract the tannic and gallic acids, then the copperas and gum were added. The iron of the copperas combined with these two inorganic acids to form the black pigment, which today is called gallotannate of iron. The gum arabic gives viscosity to the fluid to produce an even flow from a quill pen, and also helps to prevent feathering of the writing should the paper be insufficiently sized. Besides the formation of the black pigment, gallotannate of iron, sulfuric acid was also formed during this chemical reaction. This acid is nonvolatile, and is injurious to paper fibers. Evidence of its detrimental effect on manuscripts will be presented later.

A copy of an interesting procedure for compounding this ink, circa 1483, was sent to me by Mr. L. C. Hector of the British Public Records Office, London. It may be found in that institution's Miscellanea of the Chancery 34/1/3, and is as follows:

> To make hynke, take galle and coporos or vitrial (quod idem est) and gumme, of everyche a quartryn other half quartryn, and a half quartryn of galle more, and breke the galle a ij. or a iij., and put ham togedere everyche on in a pot, and stere it ofte. Wythinne ij. wykys after ȝe mowe wryte therwyth. Yf ȝe have a quartryn of everyche, take a quarte of watre; yf halfe a quartryn of everyche, than take half a quarte of watyr.

When first made, the above formula produces very pale writings, but if the ink is aged for two or more weeks, it has sufficient blackness to distinguish the characters as they are written. These characters continue to darken, and maximum blackness is reached within thirty days. On exposure to air, the gallotannate of iron oxidizes from the ferrous to the ferric state. In the ferrous state, it is relatively colorless, and in the ferric state, it is jet black. It was this factor that prompted the inkmakers to specify in most of the formulae that the ink be stirred intermittently for about two weeks.

It was during mid-eighteenth century that Lewis found a method of overcoming this problem of giving color to freshly made iron gall inks. He experimented with the addition of various berry juices, but found them detrimental to the color of the writing when exposed to sunlight. Logwood extract was the dye he found most satisfactory for this purpose, but it was gradually replaced by other dyes. If this ink were kept corked from the air, it had far fewer solid particles, and this made its use possible in a fountain pen.

None of the earlier formulae in table 1 specify the addition of indigo. However, a blue coloring material which appears to be indigo is occasionally found in writings previous to the study of Lewis. The most probable reason for its use was to give the needed color to freshly made iron gall ink. According to the recent work of Mitchell and Hepworth, indigo was used for this purpose by Eisler in 1770, and it was later used by other workers in this field.

The addition of aqua vitae, brandy, or spirits was frequently recommended to keep ink from freezing and breaking its container. Some of the eighteenth-century inkmakers condemned this addition due to the facts that the ink faded more quickly in an inkwell and had a tendency to feather on paper when writing. However, according to the literature, freezing was a serious problem in cold climates. It is of interest to note that Campbell E. Waters, of the National Bureau of Standards, did not encounter this difficulty when he froze ink in a refrigerator.

## Ink Powders

The factors most likely responsible for the development of powdered or portable ink were the possibility of freezing and the difficulty of carrying a liquid ink on a journey. Gerolamo Ruscelli (d. 1566), Venetian scientist, and Caneparius both recommended powdering the ingredients of *encaustum* and adding as much soot "as you wish, or what may seem sufficient." When traveling, wine was added "when there was an urgent need to write." With so little time allowed to extract the gallic and tannic acids of the powered galls, this formula would basically produce a carbon ink similar to that of Dioscorides. Some gallotannate of iron would be produced by this procedure, but the amount would be small.

Another type of ink powder was made by evaporating the liquid iron gall ink in a *balneo mariae* (water bath) and powdering in residue. When a solvent was added, this ink would write as black as or blacker than it did before evaporation. A powder of this nature was compact, which made shipment much simpler, and molding and freezing were no problems under ordinary storage conditions. It was often advertised for sale in the newspapers of Virginia and other colonies during the eighteenth century, which indicates its use had become general.

It is not known when this procedure of making an ink powder was developed. Mitchell and Hepworth state that Holman was granted a patent in 1668 for its manufacture, but no description of the process was given. I have found small quantities of this powder in the inner margins of record books as early as 1680. The earliest description of the process found is in Robert Dossie's *The Handmaid to the Arts*, printed in 1764.

## Ink Containers

Many different types of containers for storing ink were suggested by the early writers. Ink powders could be stored in almost any type of container, but paper offered a simple and inexpensive method of packaging. A communication in the Executive Papers deposited at the Virginia State Library, dated 19 December 1782, from L[eighton] Wood to James Simmons requesting "half dozen papers of Ink Powders" seems to substantiate this idea.

The containers for liquid ink were not so simple as those for ink powders, and were generally made of glass, metal, horn, or wood. Lewis warned against the use of copper or lead containers, and he recommended the use of an oaken cask as it has the same astringent materials (gallic and tannic acids) as found in galls. About one hundred and fifty-five years earlier, the recommendations of Caneparius were quite different, and were as follows: "Keep the ink in a lead vase, for lead increases the blackness. The ink can be kept, however, in a glass vase, if the vase is thoroughly cleaned. You can also keep it in a vitreous potter's vase, or in a gourd which has hardened with age. Container should be kept closed or at least covered, so as to keep out the dust which will mess up the ink in a marvelous manner."

## Writings Made with Iron Gall Inks

The iron gall inks used during the period of this study have produced, in nearly all instances, writings which have retained good legibility. Those writings that have faded can, in most cases, be traced to adverse storage conditions. Light rays, mold, and bacteria are the principal agents in this respect. Originally, such writings were black, but the majority of them have gradually turned a rusty brown. It is difficult to say exactly how long it takes for this change in color, but, in my opinion, the usual time varies from about twenty-five to one hundred years. The factors effecting this change are the proportions of the ink ingredients, the amount deposited on the paper, and the composition of the paper. The action of each of these factors may be accelerated by poor storage conditions.

This color change takes place in writings produced from inks which have been compounded with insufficient gallic and tannic acid in proportion to the amount of copperas. This improper ratio exists in many of the formulae of table 1, which accounts for there being more brown than black writing in early manuscripts. A good example of these incorrect proportions may be found in the formula of Caneparius,[1] and it is as follows:

Vini albi lib. iiii, aceti acerrimi cyathus unus, gallae fractae unc. ii. admisceantur per quatuor dies, mox decoquantur vulcano usque ad evaporationem ipsius quartae partis, tunc colentur, & colaturae addere licet gummae Arabicae tritae unc. ii. & optime admiscendo exponatur igni, & bulliat tempore quo dicerentur tres pater noster, hinc tollatur ab igne, & addatur Vitrioli Romani triti unc. iii. assidue ligno agitando donec sit fere frigefactum, deinde reponatur in cucurbita vitrea, quae optime clausa teneatur soli caeloq; sereno per tres dies naturales, his expletis coletur atque servetur.

Lewis found that on exposure to sunlight, writings made of formulae of this type soon turned brown, and that a ratio of one of copperas to three of galls by weight gave the best results. This is in line with modern methods of calculating the proper proportions of these compounds.

When documents are written with ink composed of insufficient gallic and tannic acids, the excess ferrous sulfate slowly converts to a basic ferric sulfate and complex oxides of iron. These rusty brown compounds seem gradually to have an adverse effect on the black gallotannate of iron and convert it to a similarly colored compound. I have found that when exposed to sunlight, early specimens containing brown writing did not fade any faster than the black, and both had better stability than new writing of a similar formulae. It was also found that the old writings required stronger solutions of oxalic acid to eradicate them. This investigation indicates that these iron compounds are like many other chemicals which become more inert over a long period of time.

For several centuries, there have been some custodians of manuscripts and some scientists who have assumed that when writings become yel-

1. The ingredients and their proportions may be found in table 1.

lowed, this change of color was an intermediate step between the original black and complete obliteration. If this were true, the majority of the manuscripts written during the early period of this study would now be indecipherable. As previously stated, nearly all of these early manuscripts are today highly legible. This fact, along with the aforementioned inertness of rusty brown writings certainly does not justify thinking that there will be further fading if such manuscripts are properly stored.

This change in color of writings from black to brown prompted Caneparius and later scientists to attempt to revive the so-called faded ink to its original blackness. The use of gallic acid, tannic acid, ammonium sulfide, and other compounds has been tried, and in all cases the revival either was unsuccessful, badly stained the paper, or left residual compounds which may be injurious to the premanency of the manuscript. Other interesting attempts to revive faded writings are described in *Patologia e terapia del libro* by Dr. Alfonso Gallo of the Instituto di Patologia del Libro. These various treatments are to be avoided, with a few exceptions, and then they should be carried out by one who has a good understanding of the many factors involved.

## The Effects of Iron Gall Ink on the Permanency of Paper

Since Latin was the scientific language of the medieval period, it was only natural that the appropriate name of *encaustum* was given to the inks made of copperas and galls. *Encaustum* means "to burn in," which is characteristic of these inks. In fact, the sulfuric acid produced by the interaction of ferrous sulfate and the organic acids of the galls does burn into the paper, and in some cases where there are heavy deposits of ink, it burns a hole through the paper. The oxidation of paper by sulfuric acid, found in concentrated iron gall inks, is much slower but similar to that produced by fire. If this acid is present in sufficient quantities, it will migrate to surrounding areas of writing, and in time produce a dark brown, and in some instances, almost black discoloration in the paper. The latter condition is found only occasionally, but it is accompanied by extreme embrittlement of the paper, poor visibility of the writing, and difficulty in photographing. Even when the concentration of this acid is not quite so great, it still migrates to adjacent sheets, discoloring the fibers and producing reversed brown writing. In some instances, this causes confusion when reading a photographic reproduction.

It is entirely possible that observation of this migration prompted the development of letter-press copies. Occasionally, examples are found in which the acid has migrated to the opposite side of a sheet and produced brown writing not reversed. The principle of making these copies consisted of effecting rapid migration of the soluble gallotannate of iron in the ferrous state from the document to the thin copy sheet. This was accomplished by moistening the thin sheet and pressing it in contact with the original until both were somewhat dry. In due time, this migrated ink would oxidize to the black ferric state. Sometimes sugar was added to slow the drying in writings. This sugar and also gum arabic frequently caused adhesion of some of the black ink particles to the copy sheet. This was an aid in producing blackness to the letter-press copy, but the best copies were those in which migration had taken place.

Lewis was the first to write about high acidity in iron inks, and also the first to conclude that this was the cause of deterioration in many manuscripts. He tried using lime to neutralize this acid, but it adversely affected other needed properties in the inks. Placing pieces of iron in the ink was recommended for this purpose, and this did decrease the amount of acid present in the ink, but it also increased the content of copperas.

A nonacid iron ink was first discovered in 1908 by Silberman and Ozorovitz of Rumania, but a practical method of manufacture was made possible only recently by the work of the Organic Section of the National Bureau of Standards and the laboratory of the United States Government Printing Office. This new ink is composed of iron, ammonia, and gallic acid, and is technically known as diammonium hydroxyferrigallate. I have used this ink in my fountain pen for the past six years, and have found it unnecessary to clean this pen during that time. On the other hand, difficulties may be encountered if other types of iron inks are used in the pen without a thorough cleaning. While this is the greatest improvement made in iron gall inks during the past two hundred years, unfortunately it has not been placed on the market by manufacturers. The future custodian would benefit considerably from this development if its adoption should become general in creating records.

In a recent study of inks, Elmer W. Zimmerman, Charles G. Weber, and Arthur E. Kimberly of the National Bureau of Standards found that the mineral acid of iron inks was detrimental to the permanency of paper. Their experiments indicated that copperas was also injurious to paper, but that the other ingredients, such as gum arabic and tannic and gallic acids, had no adverse effect.

The studies and data previously presented might make one think that all manuscripts are suffering ill effects from iron gall inks. This is not true, but it does raise the question as to why some iron inks have caused deterioration while others have not produced any adverse effects. This prompted me to undertake a study of early ink formulae, and the data collected, as well as the results of experimentation, were published in 1948 (see Ink Bibliography).

A survey was made of early manuscripts to determine whether the brown or black writing was the most injurious to paper. Among several hundred manuscripts examined, fifty were found in which the ink had eaten holes through the paper. Three contained brown writing, and forty-seven contained black writing, which was a strong indication that the black writing was the most injurious. Tests were made on fifteen samples of seventeenth- and eighteenth-century manuscript fragments, and, as a rule, the black writings were much more acid than the brown writings. With one exception, the uninked margins were less acid than the inked areas, and in this exception, the pH was the same.

This finding was then further confirmed by preparing two inks, one with sufficient tannic and gallic acid to give permanent black writing, and another with only one-fourth as much of these acids, which will produce brown writing in a matter of time. After artificial aging of 72 hours at 100° C., papers containing lines drawn with the permanent black ink exhibited much greater decrease in the folding test and were more acid than those containing the ink which in time produces the brown writing. Each of these inks contained six grams of copperas per 100 cc. of distilled water, which is considered quite concentrated for present-day ink, although many formulae in table 1 specify much greater concentration.

When the amount of copperas is the same in two given inks, then more sulfuric acid is produced in the one containing sufficient tannic and gallic acids to react with all of the iron in the copperas than in the other ink with insufficient tannic and gallic acids which react with only part of the iron present. In other words, the amount of sulfuric acid produced is in relation to the amount of tannic and gallic acid present to react with the quantity of iron in the copperas. This, in turn, accounts for black writing being usually more acid and injurious to paper than brown writing.

It was concluded from this study that most concentrated inks which produced the black writing were the most damaging to the permanency of the paper. These inks were naturally the most acid, and there are several formulae in table 1 which would make inks of this type. Two other factors sometimes causing increased acidity were residual sulfuric acid in the copperas and evaporation of a portion of the solvent in an inkwell. Large amounts of this concentrated ink deposited in relatively small areas are also a large factor in manuscript deterioration. This can be caused by the use of a broad penpoint, close writing, and the utilization of both sides of a sheet for writing.

Many early manuscripts written with iron gall ink are in a good state of preservation. These manuscripts have relatively little or no acidity in them. Some of the factors which contribute to this condition are a narrow pen point, formation of large letters, writing on only one side of the paper, a low concentration of ink ingredients, no residual sulfuric acid in the copperas, and alkaline salts present in the paper. It will be shown later that many early papers contain alkaline salts which sometimes existed in sufficient quantities to neutralize a portion or most of the acidity in moderately acid inks.

Among those manuscripts needing restoration, many show some evidence of discoloration and deterioration from acid inks. In a few cases, the acidity of iron gall inks had been the entire reason for the need of restoration, as the inked areas are in a crumbling condition while the uninked margins are in an excellent state of preservation. With the exception of deterioration by microorganisms, fire, and light rays, acid inks have been a contributing factor in the embrittlement of a large majority of manuscripts. Unless some method of eliminating or neutralizing this nonvolatile acid is effected, it will continue its activity until the paper fibers are reduced to dust. Procedures for deacidification will be presented later.

## Red Ink

Extract of brazilwood was the coloring material most frequently used in making red ink. The raspings of this wood were allowed to soak for several days in either vinegar or urine. Gum arabic was then added to give proper viscosity for writing. Most of the formulae recommended the addition of alum, which has an adverse effect on the permanency of paper.

In John Barrow's *Dictionarium Polygraphium* of 1735, there may be found a typical example of making red ink from brazilwood, and it is as follows: "To make Red writing INK. Take rasping of Brazil one ounce, white lead and alum of each 2 drams; grind and mingle them, infuse them in urine one pound, with 2 scruples of gum arabick, or a dram at most."

This dye is highly soluble when first extracted, but after about two hundred years, writings made of this ink become relatively insoluble. This is another example of the decreased solubility of a compound as time passes. After a few decades, these writings lose their brightness, becoming a dull reddish brown, but only a few have become undecipherable due to fading.

According to the recent studies of William F. Leggett, brazilwood was known in the medieval period, and was imported from India. When the Portuguese discovered the east central part of South America, they named this country "Terra de Brazil" due to the abundance of these trees growing along the shores.

In addition to the extract of brazilwood, vermilion was another source for producing red ink. Vermilion is mercury sulfide, and is insoluble in water. It was first powdered and "sufficient to give a good color" was added to water or vinegar. The glair of eggs or gum water was also added to give viscosity and to act as an adhesive for the insoluble particles. The egg glair softens more slowly than gum arabic under high humidity, which made some of the writings less likely to smudge than others. According to Mitchell, this red ink was frequently used by the Romans to make their capital letters.

## Blue Inks

Indigo was known to the Romans as *indicum*, and was classified by several of their early writers as one of the *atramenti*. It has been used not only in inks, but also in paints, medicines, cosmetics, dyeing, bluing cloth and paper, etc. A. Lucas questions the general use of indigo by the ancients for dyeing, but thinks it was used as an ink. Dr. P. K. Gode, of Poona, India, is now trying to establish the earliest possible date of its manufacture and export to the West. Indigo was first made in India and comes from the leaf of *Indigofera tinctoria*, a member of the order Leguminosae. It was known to the Incas, and, like cochineal and brazilwood, was one of the early dyes exported from the Americas.

There are relatively few formulae to be found for making blue ink from indigo. These formulae recommended that powdered indigo be added to water containing gum arabic. Its color holds up well over a period of time, but writings made of this ink smudge during damp weather, and can be washed from the paper.

These indigo writings are unaffected by certain microorganisms that are very damaging to some inks. Recently, I had the opportunity to inspect several moldy manuscripts from tropical Guatemala and Honduras. In some areas of these manuscripts, the iron inks were obliterated, but the indigo ink was unaffected. Some dyes inhibit the growth of microorganisms, and this may account for the use of indigo by the early

Roman physicians in treating cuts and burns. Another unusual property of this type of writing is that it turns a bright blue when first laminated with cellulose acetate film, but gradually reverts to its original color within a few weeks or months. For detailed information, consult *The Library of Congress Quarterly Journal*, vol. X, no. 1 (November, 1952). The cause of this change is not definitely known, but it is thought that under heat, a very minute amount of the residual acetic acid of this film reduces a small amount of the indigo blue to indigo white. There are others who think that this could be caused by the slight solvent action of the plasticizer or a trace of sulfurous acid in the film. Applying the plasticizers to prepared specimens did not produce this change, however, and the manufacturer of the film used doubted that there was any sulfurous acid present. Regardless of the cause of this change, in time this indigo white oxidizes back to its original color.

Prussian blue (ferric ferrocyanide) was not discovered until the latter part of the seventeenth century, and it did not replace indigo as a blue ink until about the mid-eighteenth century. It gained considerable popularity as a writing ink after 1800. The formulae specified the addition of powdered Prussian blue to gum water to make a suitable writing fluid. This iron ink is unlike the iron ink made with galls as it has exhibited no evidence of injury to paper. While writings of this ink are relatively unaffected by light rays and bleaching agents, it does smudge when damp and is affected by moderately strong alkali. Many of the writings made with this ink a hundred or more years ago still retain a high degree of luster.

## Printing Ink

The ink used for early printing was composed of a pigment and a vehicle such as boiled linseed oil. Soot or some other carbon black was used in making the black inks, and the colored ones contained the pigments usually used by artists. The linseed oil served as the binder for these inks, and it oxidized and polymerized into an insoluble compound after its application to paper. These printing inks resemble the paints used by the artist more than the writing inks used by the scribe.

The black printing inks made of carbon and boiled linseed oil are the most permanent of all inks. They are not affected by light rays and bleaching agents, they are insoluble in water, and they are difficult to remove from a document without leaving evidence of alteration. If the linseed oil is properly prepared, it is not considered injurious to the permanency of the paper. Occasionally, a book is found in which there has been migration and discoloration of the oils, but this has been attributed by several to the use of fish oil or some other substitute. As a rule, these early black printing inks have held up well, and only occasionally is one found in which the binder has been injurious to the paper.

According to Caneparius, printers of his time made their ink with a varnish containing Arabian sandarac and flaxseed or nut oil which was boiled with the soot of pitch. He states that this was an improvement over a formula of soot of pitch and flaxseed oil recommended by Antonius Musa Brasarola (1500–1555), an Italian physician, botanist, and author. Caneparius further states that another ink, which he describes as almost a perpetual crust (*fere perpetuum Stuchum*), was used to fill the engraved letters on marble tablets, etc., and was composed of flaxseed oil and pitch. It is entirely possible that the early printing inks evolved from this so-called almost perpeutal crust, or ink, as they are similar in composition, and the latter was used for several centuries before the invention of printing from movable type. Caneparius thought that Brasarola was of a similar opinion, as the latter states that the ink of the chalcographer became the ink of the typographer.

Joseph Moxon recommended in his *Mechanick Exercises* (1683) that the oil be boiled, but that setting fire to it was unnecessary. He also recommended that one-half to one pound of rosin be added to each gallon of oil. He and his successors of the eighteenth century advocated the addition of bread and onions to the oil when it was boiled. Hard soap makes its appearance in the literature in the earlier part of the following century. A thorough search for early printing ink formulae and a study as to the effects of their components on paper have never been made. Information resulting from such an investigation is greatly needed by those interested in the restoration and preservation of documents.

## Other Inks

There were other writing fluids described in the literature as inks, but there is very little evidence that they were used for writing purposes. In most cases, they should be classified as water colors for illuminating manuscripts and other decorative purposes. The data on the commonly used black, red, and blue inks have been presented to give the archivist and librarian a better understanding of the various characteristics of the writings which are in their custody. A broader knowledge of ink properties will assist the custodian in evaluating good storage conditions and restoration procedures for books and manuscripts.

Table 1 Iron gall ink formulae expressed in grams per 100 c.c. of solvent

| No. | Date | Cop-eras | Galls | Gum arabic | Rock alum | Log-wood | Solvent | Other additions | Ink bibliog-raphy |
|---|---|---|---|---|---|---|---|---|---|
| 1 | 1412 | X* | X | X | | | Rain water | | 53 |
| 2 | 1483 | 12.4 | 18.6 | 12.4 | | | Water | | 5 |
| 3 | 15th C. | 10.0 | 2.5 | 2.5 | | | Rain water & vinegar | | 53 |
| 4 | " | 9.3 | 15.5 | 9.3 | | | Water | | " |
| 5 | " | 3.0 | 12.0 | 1.0 | | | Wine | | " |
| 6 | " | 4.5 | 7.5 | 0.2 | | | Beer or wine | | " |
| 7 | 1500 | 50.0 | X | 12.5 | | | Wine | | 35 |
| 8 | 1511 | 6.2 | 0.0 | 9.3 | | | | | 55 |
| 9 | 1547 | 4.0 | 0.0 | 2.0 | X | | Water | 2 Romaine galls | 3 |
| 10 | 1559 | 8.2 | 12.3 | 4.1 | | | Rain water | 4.1 g. pomegranate | 47 |
| 11 | 1564 | 8.0 | 16.0 | 8.0 | | | Wine | | " |
| 12 | 1571 | 9.3 | 15.5 | 6.2 | | | Rain water | | 14 |
| 13 | 1572 | 3.6 | 6.0 | 2.4 | | | White wine | Salt | 33 |
| 14 | 16th C. | 3.1 | 6.2 | 12.4 | | | Ale | | 35 |
| 15 | " | 3.1 | 6.2 | 12.4 | | | Spring water | | " |
| 16 | " | 9.3 | 12.4 | 12.4 | 12.4 | | Rain water | | " |
| 17 | 1602 | 9.3 | 15.5 | 6.2 | | | Wine or rain water | | 16 |
| 18 | 1619 | 3.3 | 9.9 | 6.6 | | | White wine | 9.9 g. pomegranate rind | 15 |
| 19 | " | 6.6 | 9.9 | 6.6 | | | " " | Handful ash bark | " |
| 20 | " | 2.5 | 10.5 | 5.0 | | | White wine | | " |
| 21 | " | 19.8 | 13.2 | 6.6 | | | " " | Handful nut tree branches | " |

*X denotes that the compound is specified but the quantity not given.

|  |  |  |  |  |  |  |  |  |  |
|---|---|---|---|---|---|---|---|---|---|
| 22 | 1619 | 2.5 | 10.0 | 5.0 |  |  | White wine |  | 15 |
| 23 | " | 6.0 | 4.0 | 4.0 |  |  | White wine or vinegar |  | " |
| 24 | " | 10.0 | 15.0 | 10.0 |  |  | " " " " |  | " |
| 25 | " | 12.5 | 6.2 | 6.2 |  |  | Wine from mallows |  | " |
| 26 | 1634 | X | X | X |  |  | Wine or beer |  | 13 |
| 27 | 1656-66 | 2.3 | 3.1 | 1.5 |  |  | Rain water |  | 7 |
| 28 | 1700 | 2.4 | 7.2 | 3.6 | 0.4 |  | " " | Husk of walnuts | 9 |
| 29 | 1705 | 4.0 | 6.0 | 5.0 | X |  | " " | " " " | " |
| 30 | 1727 | 1.5 | 9.3 | 6.2 | 3.1 |  | " " | Sugar loaf size of hoarselnut | 16 |
| 31 | 1734 | 37.6 | 99.2 | 3.1 |  |  | Water |  | 28 |
| 32 | " | 4.0 | 1.0 | 0.5 |  |  | Ink powder formula |  | " |
| 33 | 1735 | 6.0 | 12.0 | 6.0 | 6.0 |  | Rain water |  | 11 |
| 34 | " | 3.5 | 5.6 | X |  |  | " " |  | " |
| 35 | " | 6.3 | 6.3 | 2.1 |  |  | " " |  | " |
| 36 | " | 4.2 | 6.3 | X |  |  | " " |  | " |
| 37 | " | 6.0 | 12.0 | 6.0 |  | 24.0 | White wine | 6.0 pomegranate peels | " |
| 38 | " | 3.0 | 12.0 | 6.0 |  |  | Rain water | Feces | " |
| 39 | 1746-80 | 3.1 | 12.4 | 3.1 |  |  | Spring water |  | 1 |
| 40 | 1751-65 | 24.8 | 49.6 | 6.2 |  |  | Rain water | Salt | 23 |
| 41 | " | 8.0 | 6.0 | 2.0 | 3.0 |  | River water & white wine |  | " |
| 42 | 1753 | 6.2 | 12.4 | 6.2 |  |  | Rain water |  | 45 |
| 43 | 1754 | 6.2 | 6.2 | 2.0 |  |  | River or rain water |  | 38 |
| 44 | " | 24.8 | 62.0 | 6.2 |  |  | Water | 24.8 g. white vitriol | " |

Table 1 (cont.)

| No. | Date | Coperas | Galls | Gum arabic | Rock alum | Logwood | Solvent | Other additions | Ink Bibliography |
|---|---|---|---|---|---|---|---|---|---|
| 45 | 1754 | 0.7 | 12.5 | 0.7 | | | Rape vinegar | 0.7 g. ivory black<br>12 g. lac-seed varnish | 38 |
| 46 | 1760 | 6.2 | 12.4 | 1.5 | 1.5 | | Soft water | | 41 |
| 47 | 1763 | 3.1 | 9.3 | X | | 3.1 | Vinegar or white wine | | 31 |
| 48 | " | 6.0 | 6.0 | 2.0 | | | Rain or river water | | 39 |
| 49 | " | 4.0 | 10.0 | 1.0 | | | Ink powder formula | 2.0 g. white vitriol | " |
| 50 | " | 0.7 | 11.4 | 0.7 | | | Water | 3 g. lac-seed varnish<br>0.7 g. ivory black | " |
| 51 | 1764 | 6.2 | 12.4 | 3.9 | 1.5 | | Soft water | | 21 |
| 52 | " | 6.2 | 12.4 | 2.7 | | 12.4 | " " | 1.5 g. pomegranate peel<br>logwood or privet berries | " |
| 53 | " | 8.0 | 0.0 | 2.0 | | | " " | 8.0 g. pomegranate peel | " |
| 54 | " | 3.7 | 7.4 | 2.3 | | | Ink powder formula | | " |
| 55 | 1766 | 8.0 | 16.0 | 16.0 | | | Wine | | 6 |
| 56 | 1770 | 3.1 | 12.4 | 3.1 | | | Rain water | | 35 |
| 57 | " | 6.2 | 24.8 | 4.7 | 1.5 | | Rain water & vinegar | 0.75 g. verdigris | " |
| 58 | 1770-85 | 6.2 | 15.5 | 6.2 | | | Rain or spring water | Alum, Indies & sugar | 8 |
| 59 | 1770-87 | 5.0 | 7.5 | 7.5 | | | White wine or river water | | 1 |
| 60 | 1772 | 6.0 | 12.0 | 3.1 | | 12.0 | Rain water | 1.6 g. pomegranate peels | 6 |
| 61 | 1777 | 9.1 | 7.5 | 6.0 | | 4.1 | Water | Salammoniac to prevent molding | 35 |
| 62 | 1778 | 12.0 | 24.0 | 3.0 | | | Rain water | | 23 |
| 63 | " | 8.0 | 6.0 | 2.0 | 3.0 | | River water or wine | | " |

| | | | | | | | | | |
|---|---|---|---|---|---|---|---|---|---|
| 64 | 1792 | 4.1 | 8.2 | 4.1 | | 4.1 | Water | 1.0 g. Copper sulfate | 35 |
| 65 | 1795 | 6.2 | 15.5 | 6.2 | X | | Rain water | 3.1 g. sugar, 1 piece indigo | 4 |
| 66 | 1798 | 3.1 | 9.3 | X | | 3.1 | Vinegar or white wine | | 22 |
| 67 | 18th C. | 6.2 | 12.4 | 6.2 | | | Rain water | | 6 |
| 68 | " | 4.0 | 8.0 | 8.0 | | | " | | " |
| 69 | 1801 | 24.8 | 74.4 | 24.8 | | | Rain or river water | | 24 |
| 70 | " | 6.2 | 12.4 | 6.2 | | | Water | | " |
| 71 | 1819 | 12.4 | 31.2 | 14.5 | | | White vinegar | | 40 |
| 72 | " | 3.1 | 12.4 | 3.1 | 0.7 | 3.1 | Rain water | 0.7 g. sugar candy | " |
| 73 | 1810-24 | 9.0 | 24.0 | 9.0 | | | Water or beer | | 19 |
| 74 | " | 2.3 | 4.6 | 2.3 | | | Water | | " |
| 75 | " | 6.2 | 12.4 | 3.1 | | 12.4 | " | 1.5 g. pomegranate peels | " |
| 76 | 1825 | 6.2 | 12.4 | 3.9 | 1.4 | | " | | 32 |
| 77 | " | 3.1 | 9.3 | 3.1 | | 3.1 | " | | " |
| 78 | " | 8.0 | 16.0 | 4.0 | | | Rain water | | " |
| 79 | " | 2.4 | 9.9 | 3.7 | | 2.4 | Water | 0.3 g. copper acetate<br>1.8 g. sugar | 32 |
| 80 | " | 12.4 | 0.0 | 3.1 | | | " | 12.4 g. pomegranate peels | " |
| 81 | " | 8.0 | 16.0 | 5.0 | | | Ink powder formula | 3 g. pomegranate peels | " |
| 82 | 1838 | 4.0 | 6.0 | 4.0 | | | Water | | 43 |
| 83 | 1842 | 6.2 | 12.4 | 3.9 | 1.5 | | " | | 51 |
| 84 | " | 6.2 | 12.4 | 6.9 | 1.5 | 12.4 | " | 0.7 g. pomegranate peels | " |
| 85 | " | 13.6 | 0.0 | 3.4 | | | " | 13.6 g. " " | " |
| 86 | " | 8.0 | 16.0 | 5.0 | | | Ink powder formula | 3 g. " " | " |

## Summary

Among the inks discussed in this chapter, the iron gall ink has proved to be far more damaging to papers than any of the other inks. It is impossible to make this ink by the old formulae without creating sulfuric acid, which is the principal, or at least a contributing agent to the deterioration of many manuscripts needing restoration. Writings made with iron gall ink have turned a rusty brown in many instances, but these complex oxides of iron are very stable compounds under normal storage conditions. As a whole, iron gall ink may be considered the best record ink developed.

The carbon, indigo, Prussian blue, and vermilion inks have good color stability, but they smudge easily during very damp weather, and can be washed from the paper. The water-soluble red extract of brazilwood is not light-fast, but as time passes it becomes less soluble and has retained its color reasonably well under favorable storage conditions. As a whole, printing inks have exhibited relatively little injury to paper, but more research is needed regarding their effects on paper. Also, additional research is needed on the other inks mentioned above.

# III Paper

FROM the earliest times to the present, the cellulose fiber has been a most important material for recording the writings of mankind. This fiber gives physical strength to papyrus, cloth, wood, palm leaves, paper, and many other materials that have been used for writing and printing. Paper has replaced all of the other materials for this purpose, and also the much-used parchment and vellum of the medieval period.

Basically, paper consists of fabricated cellulose fibers and a sizing material such as animal glue or starch. Its physical strength is derived from the individual fibers as well as fiber-to-fiber bonding. The size controls the rate of absorption of ink and aids in the bonding of the fibers. The principal sources of this fiber are linen, cotton, hemp, jute, straw, and wood. The type of fiber used at different times depended upon its availability in at least a partially purified state. In the raw state, these fibers contain fats, waxes, and in some cases lignin, etc., which must be removed before a fiber of high purity is obtained.

When the art of papermaking was first introduced in Europe, linen was the fiber generally available. Cotton was used also, but it was a costly fiber and did not become common until after the invention of the cotton gin by Eli Whitney in 1793. Rags or clippings of linen and cotton cloth were the principal source of the cellulose fiber used in the manufacture of writing and printing papers during the period of this study. Hemp, jute, and straw also appear in the papermaking literature during the eighteenth and nineteenth centuries, but these fibers were most often used for making wrapping paper and similar products. It was not until several years after the discovery of chlorine by Karl Wilhelm Scheele in 1774 that it was possible to bleach these fibers sufficiently to use them in low-grade writing and printing papers. Evidence substantiating these statements may be found in the early and recent studies on papermaking, and particularly in the late studies of both Dard Hunter and R. H. Clapperton.

Cotton is the purest cellulose fiber occurring in nature, and requires but little chemical treatment before it can be made into paper. Linen must first go through a retting process (the removal of noncellulostic materials by microorganisms) before it is suitable even for weaving.

Both of these fibers must be bleached to make them white enough for writing and printing papers. When properly processed and stored, these two fibers have a high degree of permanency. Hunter states that the earliest dated paper is from A.D. 264, and there are undated specimens which are thought to have been made about a hundred years earlier. The generally accepted date for the invention of paper is A.D. 105. Lucas has examined pieces of linen cloth estimated to be seven thousand years old. Some of the earliest papyri, which also depend upon the cellulose fiber for physical strength, have been estimated by Lucas to be about five thousand years old. The studies of Leggett show that recently excavated linen fibers are estimated to be ten thousand or more years old. It may be said that this fiber is very stable and will last almost indefinitely if unaffected by certain agents which are destructive.

Custodians do not always fully appreciate the efforts made by the early papermakers to produce a lasting and durable paper. Many of them have concluded that the procedures and materials used by these craftsmen came about by accident and not by intelligent planning. There is much evidence in the literature indicating that considerable thought was given to producing a paper of high quality. A great deal of their knowledge was gained by trial and error, but observations of their predecessors' products were likewise a factor.

An unsigned German manuscript of the late sixteenth century, translated by Blanchet in 1900, stressed many points which enter into good papermaking procedures. This was true of other writers, and particularly true of Father Imberdis, who lived in France during the seventeenth century. His treatise on papermaking was also translated by Blanchet. Imberdis was the first to recommend certain specifications for paper to be used in writing fine books which should be expected to last for centuries. He advised "That it be white, that sad wrinkles do not streak it, and that bold roughness does not stand out on its surface." To test paper for sufficient sizing, he recommends that "Shaken in the hand the paper will not fall like a rag, but like parchment it will ring . . ." and, "Cover it with saliva; if on any point moisture deposited on its surface does not come out on the reverse side, do not question it."

## Rags for Papermaking

When a comparison is made of papers made during the fifteenth century with those of the following century, little or no difference in their structure is apparent. Therefore, if technical treatises of the fifteenth century on the art of papermaking were available, most likely the procedures used would be the same as described in the literature of the sixteenth and seventeenth centuries. During these two latter centuries, the writers on this subject stressed the importance of using new, strong rags for the best grades of writing and printing papers. The worn and discolored rags were generally used for making wrapping paper, cartridge paper, blotting paper, pasteboard, and so forth. This practice accounts for the fact that many of the records of these centuries are in an excellent state of preservation. Toward the end of the seventeenth century, the demand for paper became great, and soon the supply of new white rags was insufficient to fill the needs. The buyers of paper, and especially those in the colonies which were in the soft currency areas, were often forced to purchase any quality available. They were soon buying inferior papers made of a large percentage of worn and deteriorated rags. This practice of using low-grade rags for making paper was condemned often by the writers of the eighteenth century.

The addition of bluing to paper made of yellowed and deteriorated rags gave the yellowed paper a relatively white appearance. This optical illusion, or gentle art of faking, may have fooled many purchasers of paper, as for centuries whiteness had been looked upon as a sign of purity. This addition made possible the use of low-grade rags in making writing and printing papers. Further camouflaging of low-grade and certain dyed rags was accomplished by dyeing the paper blue. Some of these colored rags, which could be redyed blue, were new and could be made into a strong and lasting paper. The art of bluing was well understood by the cloth bleachers, as the *Cyclopaedia* of 1728, by Ephraim Chambers, mentions smalt, Dutch lapis, and indigo for bluing.

During the eighteenth century, sulfur dioxide and oil of vitriol (sulfuric acid) were mentioned in connection with the bleaching of cloth, but nothing appears in the literature to indicate that it was used in the bleaching of rags for papermaking. The use of sulfur dioxide for whitening linen cloth was mentioned by Pliny in the first century. About the end of the eighteenth century, chlorine became the agent for whitening the yellowed, deteriorated, and colored rags. A description of the procedures used in this process appears in volume XIII of Dobson's *Encyclopaedia* (Philadelphia, 1798). The indiscriminate use of this compound caused much deterioration within the cellulose fibers, and in many instances produced a paper of high acidity. The lack of controlled methods in its application accounts for much of the deterioration found in papers of the nineteenth century. For technical data on the effects of chlorine on paper, it is suggested that the following bibliography be consulted: *Permanence and Durability of Paper*, by Morris S. Kantrowitz, Ernest W. Spencer, and Robert H. Simmons.

From about 1700 onward, the demand for paper became greater, and the quality progressively worse. Rags of all sorts and conditions were treated in various and sundry ways to produce fairly white stuff for the making of paper. According to Hunter, even the linen wrappings of the ancient mummies of Egypt were robbed and sold for this purpose during the nineteenth century. Besides the low physical strength of many of these rags and wrappings, quite a few contained almost every conceivable type of foreign matter. Fortunately, some of it was washed out during the papermaking processes. Even under modern methods of purification, old, used rags do not make a strong paper. This statement is well substantiated by the findings of Merle B. Shaw, George W. Bicking, and Martin J. O'Leary of the National Bureau of Standards in *A Study of the Relation of Some Properties of Cotton Rags to the Strength and Stability of Experimental Papers Made from Them*. These investigators also found that papers made of low-grade rags lacked good stability. The use of low-grade rags accounts for some of the papers made after 1700 being in a weakened condition today. The indiscriminate use of chlorine after its discovery in 1774 is also a factor in the deterioration of many documents.

Manuscripts that were written before 1700 with ink of low acidity and which have been properly stored are, as a rule, in a good state of preservation. Until this date, no method was employed to bleach or camouflage discolored rags as the supply of clean, new white rags or clippings from garment making was sufficient to meet the demand for writing and printing papers. At that time, the method of bleaching or whitening the cloth was relatively noninjurious to the fibers. Basically, this process consisted of first washing the cloth with soap and water, and then soaking for several hours in lye water. This lye was an extract of wood ashes, and contained the carbonates and phosphates of sodium, potassium, magnesium, and calcium. This operation in bleaching was followed by rinsing in water and spreading on the grass in a meadow with intermittent wetting. The action of sunlight, moisture, residual lye, and oxygen from the grass were all factors in this bleaching. The cloth was afterwards soaked in milk or sour bran. All of these operations were repeated until the desired whiteness was obtained, which usually took from four to six weeks. After the bleaching, the cloth was starched and whitened by the addition of chalk (calcium carbonate) and bluing. Data will be presented later which indicate that the calcium carbonate from the lye and chalk has had a beneficial effect on the permanency of many of these early papers. It is not known when this method was discovered, but R. S. Hatch, one of the contributing authors of *Cellulose and Cellulose Derivatives*, edited by Emil Ott, states that a similar method was used by the ancients.

## Preparation of Stuff

After the rags were sorted for color and quality, they were washed in a container called a puncheon which had holes at various intervals to allow water to drain from the rags. When well washed, they were then placed in small piles and allowed to ferment for four to five days. They were watched carefully for any tendency "to mildew, discolour, and take fire." When "fermented sufficiently," the rags were cut into one-half inch pieces and beat in slowly circulating water with large stamping hammers for about twelve hours. After this operation, the half stuff thus formed was placed in large wooden boxes while wet and "mellowed a week, more or less, according to the weather." After this mellowing period, they were beaten a second time and again allowed another period of "mellowing." This was known as the second stuff, which was beaten a third time in "the pit mortar." This macerated material, called stuff, was used to form the sheets of paper.

Today, many do not look upon fermentation as a method of purification, but as one of contamination. This procedure of fermentation by the early papermakers did remove the insoluble starches and other materials used in sizing cloth. The action of various enzymes produced by the different microorganisms converted the starches to soluble compounds and liquefied any animal glue present. This greatly simplified the beating operation as these undesired products could then be washed from the rags. Imberdis describes this fermentation process as "either the rag loses here a needless liquid or it softens and becomes less difficult to triturate or finally like manure, it acquires there an unknown virtue." In many instances, there was likely some loss in cellulose when this process was allowed to continue too long. The workers were continually warned to watch this process and "not let it ferment needlessly." The "Hollander," a type of beater invented just before 1682, eventually eliminated this procedure. Regardless of possible criticism of the fermentation process, the early papermakers did produce artistic and very stable papers by this method.

Water was a most necessary item for washing rags and forming the sheet of paper. Several of the early treatises stress the importance of using the purest water available. Imberdis recommended that a mill be placed above the city or village in order that no rubbish or trash contaminate the stream. He states, "In my eyes a stream is excellent for paper when, across its crystalline waves, shine numerous pebbles and the trout, abundantly speckled on the sides, leap about and frolic in close schools." This type of stream reminds one of those in a somewhat mountainous area. Frequently, the bicarbonate of calcium is found in such waters.

Washing and drying the rags in this type of hard water would precipitate small amounts of calcium carbonate in the cellulose fibers. This is another possible source of this compound found in many papers, and, as previously stated, data relative to its beneficial effect on paper will be presented later. For many years, calcium carbonate has been considered an essential ingredient in the soil which produces the grapes for the fine wines of France, Germany, Spain, Portugal, and Italy. In America, it is needed in the water used in making good sour mash whiskey and in raising the best jumping horses.

Judging from the literature, the workmen were constantly reminded of fire hazards and were encouraged to keep the mill and equipment clean and in good working order. The unsigned German manuscript translated by Blanchet recommends the following: "Be careful not to go upon the piles (rags) with dirty shoes, so that the mud does not fall in the stuff and does not soil the paper which is being made." The ferrous metals were generally prohibited in certain parts of the equipment as they would rust and damage the paper.

## Forming the Sheet

After the fibers had been properly prepared by beating, they were transfered to a vat in preparation for forming the sheet of paper. It was desirable to have the right proportions of stuff or pulp to the amount of water in order to form paper of a given thickness. The frame used in making the sheet of paper consisted of small brass wires either woven or laid parallel across a rectangular wooden frame. This frame was plunged into the vat containing the fibers suspended in water, and shaken when removed from the liquid. During the shaking motion the fibers became interlaced and interlocked as the water drained from the stuff through the wires. The wet sheet was transferred to felts, and pressed to remove the surplus water. After the pressing operation, it was hung up on hair ropes to dry.

Forming the sheet required a craftsman of good physical strength and considerable skill. The even distribution of fibers over a sheet, so often found in many old books, is a remarkable accomplishment of these early papermakers. A highly skilled craftsman can produce a sheet with about an equal number of fibers lying in each direction. This is better than can be accomplished on a machine, yet, on the other hand, a machine makes paper more uniform in thickness. There are a few admirers of handmade paper who claim that forming a sheet by hand gives greater permanence to the paper. To concur with this opinion would be the same as agreeing with one who claims that handpumped water tastes better than that pumped by a motor. The chemical purity of new strong fibers is the factor of primary importance in this respect.

## Sizing of Paper

After the newly fabricated sheet was thoroughly dry, a "cool temperate" day was selected for the sizing operation. The object of this process was to render the paper less absorbent, thus preventing ink from feathering. Imberdis stated that size was made by boiling the ears of mutton and cattle in water, and that sometimes the intestines were used. Writers of the eighteenth century recommended the parings from tanners, curriers, and parchment-makers. These later writers specified the addition of alum and, occasionally, white vitriol. The previously mentioned bluing was sometimes added to give the eighteenth- and nineteenth-century papers made of old and yellowed rags the appearance of being white. The new sheets of paper were lowered into this gelatinous solution long enough for them to become saturated, then removed and air dried.

Printing papers require much less size than writing papers due to the nature of the two inks. For good writing properties, a certain amount of size is needed, but when there is an excess of this amount there is an increase in stiffness and a decrease of flexibility within the sheet. On the other hand, a small amount of size increases the physical strength of an unsized sheet. This increase in physical strength may have caused a few archivists and librarians to conclude that resizing old paper is a worthwhile procedure as they are of the opinion that this size perishes over a period of time. With the exception of moldy documents or some other unusual condition, this size does not necessarily deteriorate. About twelve years ago, ten writing papers of the seventeenth and eighteenth centuries were submitted to the Bureau of Standards for testing. They had from 2.6 to 5.8 percent glue, which was no indication that the sizing had perished. No starch or resin was found in these papers. As a rule, these early writing papers do not exhibit feathering when written on with modern ink, which proves that they have retained at least a large portion of the original sizing. This does not apply to early printing papers as relatively little sizing was needed. It would be of interest if those who advocate this practice of resizing old papers offered data showing approximately how much physical strength was added by this procedure.

It is not known when alum was first used in the sizing of paper, but it was mentioned in the *Diary* of John Evelyn in 1678. It does not appear again in papermaking literature until about mid-eighteenth century. It was used to harden the size, which, in turn, lowered the rate of absorption in paper and further prevented feathering of ink. This alum was potassium aluminium sulfate in a somewhat unpurified state. It increased the acidity of the paper, which is an undesirable condition for documents of permanent value. White vitriol (zinc sulfate) occasionally appears in the same literature with alum, but whether it was used to any extent is not known. As a rule, sulfates are considered somewhat harmful to paper, but more information is needed relative to this particular compound.

## Polishing

The object of polishing paper is to give it a smooth surface for writing. A wolf's tooth or a polished pebble was recommended by Imberdis for this purpose, while others suggested various types of smooth stones or flints. In order to make playing cards smooth and more easily manipulated, these stones were rubbed over sheep's tallow before polishing. This practice was forbidden on writing paper as any deposit of tallow would hinder the proper penetration of ink.

Another method of imparting smoothness to the surface was by pressing a group of papers in a screw press. Later, they were removed and restacked to allow each sheet to be pressed again in contact with a new surface. Repeating this procedure several times gave additional smoothness to a sheet. Another method of applying pressure and polishing, but less commonly used, was by beating a group of papers with a mallet or hammer. All of these methods eventually gave way to the calender rolls which polished paper much more efficiently. According to the recent investigation of Julius Grant, calendering was introduced in England in 1830.

## The Finished Paper

We are indebted to the early and highly skilled craftsman for producing such beautiful, and, in many cases, permanent papers. When first made, in all probability these papers were a very light cream color. This was due to the limitations of the bleaching methods then available. The previously mentioned Ruscelli of the sixteenth century stated that an ink made of powdered white egg shells which had been bleached in the sun would produce writing easily read on the whitest of papers. From this statement, it can be concluded that these early papers were never as white as we know paper today.

In addition to the good efforts of the papermaker, the inkmaker endeavored to make an ink that produced writing of great blackness and "splendor." The skill of the scribe also contributed to making many manuscripts real works of art. The occasional use of shining sand, which appeared to be fine particles of mica, gave some of the writings a unique sparkle. The creation of many early manuscripts required the best efforts of many skilled and artistic craftsmen.

## Data Obtained by the National Bureau of Standards from Tests on Early Papers

In 1939, ten record papers of the seventeenth and eighteenth centuries were given to the National Bureau of Standards for testing. A summary of the results obtained are as follows: The fiber analyses revealed that "most of these [papers] appear to be all linen fibers but [samples] 9 and 10 obviously contain some cotton and the others may. The fibers are in such poor condition that definite differentiation between linen and cotton was not possible." The acidity of the eight papers low in physical strength varied from pH 4.0 to 4.3 by cold extraction, while those two papers in relatively good condition had pH 5.8 and 6.5. Eight of these papers had an ash content of from 0.8 to 4.2 percent, and six of these papers contained calcium carbonate or "any rare earth carbonates" in varying amounts. Since the acidity was high in the eight papers of low physical strength, it was natural to conclude that this was one of the principal causes of deterioration. This acidity and a high ash content caused some speculation as to the source of these compounds.

## Other Test Data Obtained with the Assistance of Robb and Moody

About five years ago, the firm of Robb and Moody, chemists of Richmond, Virginia, were employed to analyze the ash of eight other papers of the seventeenth and eighteenth centuries. The ash varied from .99 to 4.18 percent, and was composed primarily of silicia, aluminum, calcium, magnesium, potassium, sulfates, phosphates, and small amounts of iron and sodium. The hypothetical combinations of these elements would indicate the presence of potassium aluminum sulfate or alum which was used in the sizing operation. The calcium and magnesium salts could have been carbonates, phosphates, and sulfates which likely came from first, the lye made of wood ashes used in bleaching the cloth; second, the water containing the bicarbonates of these metals used in the papermaking process; and third, the calcium could also be from chalk used in whitening the cloth after bleaching. The silica may have come from the above-mentioned lye, bleaching meadows, water, and many other sources. The iron also had many possible sources, but much of it may have been an impurity in the alum. In two papers, nickel was found which was possibly from pulverized greenish blue glass or a type of smalt used as bluing to camouflage the yellowed rags used in making the paper. In these two papers, relatively large amounts of silica were found which further indicated the presence of ground glass.

The tests for acidity and folding endurance of these eight papers were made in my laboratory. Two of these papers were in excellent condition, and had a high folding endurance. The acidity of the one made circa 1675 was quite low (pH 6.6) and the other, made circa 1722, was slightly alkaline (pH 7.6). In both papers, the amount of calcium and magnesium was much in excess of the aluminum and potassium. Originally, the calcium and magnesium salts were likely alkaline carbonates and phosphates, while the potassium and aluminum salts were the probable acid alum.

Three of these papers had a relatively low folding endurance, and the acidity was somewhat high, with a pH 4.5 to 4.7. The amounts of calcium and magnesium were only slightly more than the aluminum and potassium. The other three papers were very weak with almost no folds recorded on the testing machine. The acidity was much higher, with a range from pH 4.1 to 4.5. This was likely due to the acid alum, as the aluminum and potassium were in excess of the calcium and magnesium.

## Findings of Other Investigators

It may be concluded from the preceding investigation that the predominating alkaline salts of calcium and magnesium have been a factor in the preservation of two of these papers. On the other hand, the acid alum ($AlK(SO_4)_2$) has had a deteriorative effect on the paper when occurring in sufficient quantities. Similar findings were made by Merle B. Shaw and Martin O'Leary of the National Bureau of Standards, when they added calcium carbonate as a filler to modern book papers and subjected them to artificial aging. The stability of these papers made with low-grade fibers was increased considerably by the addition of this carbonate.

The investigation of W. V. Torrey and E. Sutermeister of the S. D. Warren Company on three early Chinese and two European papers of the fifteenth and sixteenth centuries indicated that calcium compounds were in the two latter papers. They reported these two papers were alkaline and in good condition. Harry F. Lewis, of the Institute of Paper

Chemistry, also found calcium compounds in certain leaves of a book printed in 1576. These leaves were likewise alkaline and in good condition, while others in the same book were acid, discolored, and physically weak.

## Conclusions

It may be concluded from these various tests on early papers that the investigators found that high acidity was associated with deterioration. On the other hand, when mildly alkaline calcium compounds, and in some instances, magnesium compounds, occurred in sufficient quantities, the papers were in good condition. These papers were either slightly alkaline or contained relatively little acid. Some of these investigators further concluded that these alkaline compounds had prevented the papers from becoming acidic due to various agents during storage. The historical and test data that I have presented indicate that one of the principal sources of this high acidity was alum in the sizing, and the alkaline compounds were from lye made of wood ashes for bleaching cloth, from hard water in the papermaking process, and from chalk for whitening the cloth.

# IV Storage Conditions

IN ADDITION to the various injurious compounds found in both inks and papers, there are certain conditions of storage which adversely affect the permanency of a document. In some cases, these conditions of storage activate the injurious compounds present in many documents. The principal agents causing deterioration during storage are light, high temperature, microorganisms, acidic gases of the air, etc. It is not the purpose of this publication to discuss in detail the activity and control of these harmful agents. A summary of each is presented, however, in order to acquaint the archivist and librarian with the types of injurious compounds sometimes left in the paper as a result of adverse storage conditions.

## Polluted Air

Many libraries and archives now have equipment to remove the harmful acidic gases generally found in the air of cities as a result of the combustion of certain fuels. Among these acidic gases, sulfur dioxide is the most prevalent. This acidic compound is readily absorbed by paper, and causes deterioration of the cellulose fibers. The investigation of T. D. Jarrell, J. M. Hankins, and F. P. Veitch, of the U. S. Department of Agriculture, showed the following characteristics in the margins of books stored in urban areas: they were more acid, contained more soluble sulfates, and were physically more brittle than were the center portions of the same books. These investigators attributed this condition primarily to the deteriorative sulfur dioxide in the air. The investigations of Arthur E. Kimberly and Adelaide L. Emley also indicated that sulfur dioxide causes deterioration in paper. The test data obtained in both of these investigations showed that papers in a deteriorating condition were highly acid. This condition existed not only in the papers tested of the eighteenth and nineteenth centuries but also of the early twentieth century.

## Light Rays

Windows have been eliminated in the storage areas of many modern archives and libraries because of the adverse effects of light rays on papers and many inks. Many custodians have observed the devastating effects of light on both paper and inks when manuscripts were removed from frames or exhibit cases after being displayed for a long period of time. Lewis states that, "Cellulose, after irradiation in oxygen continues to break down even when stored in the dark," and this "post-irradiation effect can be stopped by storage in the dark in nitrogen or in helium." This recommendation was intended for documents after their removal from temporary display, but he strongly advised against exhibiting a document for a long period of time.

The investigations made by Herbert F. Launer and William K. Wilson, of the National Bureau of Standards, and George A. Richter, of the Brown Company, confirmed the fact that light rays are highly destructive to papers. In many samples of exposed paper, there was an increase in acidity together with a decided loss in physical strength. Both found alkaline buffer salts somewhat helpful in retarding this deterioration. Light rays also adversely affect the color of many inks. Since sunlight is needed for the growth of nearly all forms of plant life, it is difficult to realize that these rays are highly injurious to the cellulose fiber. However, it should be remembered that this is one of the ways in which nature breaks down and gradually eliminates the vast amount of waste cellulose occurring in dead organic plants.

Books stored in areas lighted by sunlight often exhibit the ill effects of radiant energy. The edges or outer margins of the leaves become discolored, and in the case of low-grade papers this discoloration often extends one or more inches toward the center of the leaves. Cracks soon form in these margins after a little wear, and the book becomes unusable prematurely. The leaves of books made of good rag paper generally do not discolor, but they likewise become weak and brittle. Similar examples of light damage may be found in documents and pictures that have been framed and exhibited for a period of time. Black printing ink blocks these rays, and sheets used to back the pictures or documents are discolored in those areas not in back of the inked images. Discoloration of this type has been found on the third backing sheet from the picture or document. This injury by light rays is not just confined to the surface areas of papers, but it penetrates to a greater depth than is generally realized.

## High Temperatures

A relatively high temperature activates most of the injurious compounds found in documents. The present laboratory method of aging paper is based on this principle of heating papers at a certain temperature for a given length of time. Therefore, storing documents near a radiator, or in an unventilated attic is undesirable.

Recent tests of fire-damaged records indicate that very high temperatures do considerable damage to papers. The length of time and the degree of the heat are both factors in the extent of the damage that may be expected. The folding endurance of two early-nineteenth-century records which had been damaged by fire was tested in order to determine the area most affected in a book or pile of manuscripts. Of course, the charred edges could not be tested, and the yellowed area was likewise found to be too brittle. The area extending three-fourths of an inch from the charred edge lost 94 percent of its folding endurance in comparison with the center area of the sheet. Other tests on the area one and one-half inches from the charred edge indicated a loss in folding endurance of 31 percent. There was relatively no change in the acidity of the yellowed area in comparison with the center portion of the sheet.

## High Humidity

For good flexibility, paper needs a certain amount of moisture, but if it remains too damp for a period of time the growth of microorganisms is promoted, and deterioration takes place in both paper and many inks. This type of deterioration is a problem in all climates from the Arctic Circle to the Equator. Of course, the tropics and semitropics are the areas in which paper is damaged most in this respect. Besides its dependence upon moisture, the rate of growth and propagation of microorganisms is generally accelerated by an increased temperature. When the temperature is increased beyond that of our warmest climates, however, growth is usually inhibited, and very high temperatures will kill microorganisms. The most effective manner of stopping the activity of microorganisms is control of the humidity by air conditioning.

There are many microorganisms which will attack the cellulose fibers of the paper, but an even larger group will digest the animal glue and starch used for sizing. Many of these organisms function best in an acid medium, but as T. D. Beckwith, W. H. Swanson, and T. M. Iiams point out, many fungi have their own buffer systems. These gentlemen also state that in most cases, but not all, color is produced during fermentation.

After a relatively long exposure to high humidity, these organisms will convert the animal and starch sizing to other compounds, and the fibers of the paper become soft, spongy, and very weak. This weakening of a paper is quite different from deterioration caused by high acidity as the latter is brittle and cracks easily when bent. During the fermentation process, the writings made with iron gall and a few other inks will become partially or entirely faded. No satisfactory method has been found for reviving the color of these inks. In most instances, damage to documents in this respect has resulted from storing them in damp places, and the failure to dry them quickly after a flood, or a similar soaking. Worthwhile procedures and equipment for drying water-soaked documents have been described by John S. Still of the Ohio State Museum. In the particular situation which he described, there were thousands of water-soaked manuscripts and books to be dried. Due to quick action in organizing a large and intelligent group of workers (mostly college students), the drying was accomplished within a few days after the accident, thus preventing the formation of mold. Remedial measures are also described by Robert M. Hamilton in the April 1953 issue of *The American Archivist.*

## Migration

In a recent investigation, it was found that many components in low-grade or impermanent papers migrate to other papers stored in contact with them. Many of these compounds, frequently found to be acidic, are considered injurious to the permanence of paper, and often cause discoloration which depreciates the aesthetic value of a document. The papers or paper products that often cause this damage to documents are file folders, interleaving sheets, end sheets, bookmarkers, coverboards, and so forth.

The sources of many of these injurious compounds can be found in the fibers of papers made of ground wood, jute, straw, and hemp which have had little or no chemical purification. In the natural state, these fibers have many noncellulose components which in time break down into other compounds which adversely affect the stability of the cellulose fiber. There are residual chemicals often left in paper from paper-making processes which are also migratory and injurious. Records stored adjacent to photostats (containing residual hypo) and cellulose nitrate film can also become discolored and acidic. Additional information may be found in my article, "Migration of Impurities in Papers," which appears in the 1953 issue of *Archivum*.

## Insects and Rodents

Many insects, and especially the commonly called bookworm, damage documents by eating holes through the paper. As a rule, this weakening of a sheet may be classified as a physical mutilation, and not a chemical degradation of the fibers. The occasional exception may be certain excreta deposited on a sheet by these insects. The above conditions may also be caused by mice and rats.

## Summary

When paper is subjected to the above deteriorative agents, there are many complex compounds formed by a breakdown of the paper components, and in some instances new compounds are absorbed by the paper. The composition of most of these newly formed compounds is unknown, but test data have shown that many are acidic. The resultant condition of the paper generally indicates a moderate to strong increase in acidity. This condition is considered undesirable for papers which are expected to last.

# V Deacidification

IN 1939, when the National Bureau of Standards sent me a copy of the test data discussed in chapter 3, it was observed that all of the eight deteriorated record papers were highly acid. Further investigation in my laboratory showed high acidity in other deteriorated papers of the seventeenth, eighteenth, and nineteenth centuries. The investigation of Jarrell, Hankins, and Veitch on record papers of the eighteenth and nineteenth centuries indicated similar findings. This was likewise true of the book papers they tested of the nineteenth and twentieth centuries. The books examined by Kimberly and Emley, discussed in "A Study of the Deterioration of Book Papers in Libraries," exhibited similar results in respect to acidity. Additional data may be found in table 2, which contains recent tests and some that I have reported previously. The difference in the acidity of the inked area of manuscripts and the uninked margins is reported in two of these groups. All of these papers were made for writing purposes and generally the degree of embrittlement was in relation to the amount of acid present. From the aforementioned studies and the data contained in table 2, the conclusion may be drawn that in nearly all instances deteriorated papers are highly acid (pH below 5.0).

Table 2 Acidity of manuscripts and blank papers

Group A: These specimens were quite brittle and definitely in need of restoration.

| Approximate date | No. of sides written on | pH of uninked margin | pH of inked area |
|---|---|---|---|
| | | Black writing | |
| 1669 | 2 | 4.4 | 3.7 |
| 1712 | 1 | 4.8 | 4.0 |
| 1715 | 2 | 4.3 | 3.4 |
| 1740 | 2 | 4.2 | 3.5 |
| 1769 | 2 | — | 4.6 |
| 18th C. | 1 | — | 4.1 |
| | | Brown writing | |
| 1710 | 2 | 5.1 | 4.1 |
| 1725 | 1 | 4.9 | 4.2 |
| 1745 | 1 | 5.0 | 4.8 |

Group A (cont.)

| | | | |
|---|---|---|---|
| 1747 | 2 | 4.7 | 4.4 |
| 1760 | 2 | 4.9 | 4.0 |
| 1770 | 1 | 4.9 | 4.7 |
| 1774 | 1 | — | 4.5 |
| 1784 | 1 | — | 4.7 |
| 1799 | 2 | 4.4 | 4.2 |
| 1811 | 1 | 4.8 | 4.5 |
| 1818 | 1 | 4.0 | 4.4 |
| 1819 | 2 | — | 4.7 |

Blank sheets

| Approximate date | pH of paper | Approximate date | pH of paper |
|---|---|---|---|
| 1720 | 4.4 | 1789 | 4.5 |
| 1721 | 4.5 | 1789 | 4.4 |
| 1732 | 4.5 | 1790 | 4.6 |
| 1735 | 4.3 | 1790 | 4.5 |
| 1745 | 4.1 | 1791 | 4.3 |
| 1747 | 4.0 | 1806 | 4.1 |
| 1750 | 4.1 | 1809 | 3.9 |
| 1760 | 4.7 | 1815 | 4.5 |
| 1762 | 3.6 | 1824 | 4.0 |
| 1762 | 4.1 | 1827 | 3.9 |
| 1762 | 4.0 | 1834 | 4.5 |
| 1764 | 4.2 | 1837 | 4.3 |
| 1769 | 4.5 | 1842 | 4.4 |
| 1770 | 3.7 | 1843 | 4.1 |
| 1772 | 4.1 | 1847 | 4.3 |
| 1775 | 4.4 | 1855 | 4.5 |
| 1782 | 4.1 | | |

Group B: These blank record papers were somewhat deteriorated and had low folding endurance, but were not as brittle as those in Group A.

| Approximate date | pH of paper | Approximate date | pH of paper |
|---|---|---|---|
| 1694 | 4.7 | 1790 | 4.8 |
| 1710 | 4.7 | 1795 | 4.9 |
| 1760 | 4.9 | 1795 | 4.8 |
| 1760 | 4.8 | 1799 | 4.7 |
| 1764 | 4.6 | 1820 | 4.8 |
| 1764 | 4.5 | 1840 | 5.0 |
| 1789 | 4.8 | 1857 | 4.6 |

Group C: These specimens of manuscripts, record papers, and printing papers were in good condition and had a relatively high folding endurance.

| Approximate date | No. of sides written on | pH of uninked margins | pH of inked area |
|---|---|---|---|
| 1550 | 0 | 6.7 | — |
| 1550 | 0 | 6.4 | — |
| 1560 | 0 | 6.6 | — |
| 1599* | 0 | 6.6 | — |
| 1668 | 1 | 5.6 | 5.6 |
| 1690 | 2 | 6.4 | 5.4 |
| 1708 | 1 | 5.4 | 5.4 |
| 1722* | 0 | 7.6 | — |
| 1744 | 1 | 5.1 | 5.1 |
| 1810 | 0 | 5.0 | — |
| 1819 | 0 | 6.0 | — |
| 1820 | 1 | 5.4 | 5.5 |

*Printing paper.
*Note.* The pH of these papers was determined colorimetrically, and the method of preparation of the sample was the same as that developed by Herbert F. Launer of the National Bureau of Standards. The deterioration of the paper in groups A and B could not be attributed to microorganisms.

This acid condition may be attributed to many possible sources, but the principal ones that have been found and are described in chapters 2, 3, and 4 are iron gall inks, alum in the sizing, chlorine in the bleach, and acidic compounds acquired from adverse storage conditions. For many decades, acidity has been regarded by paper scientists as one of the most destructive enemies of paper. Unless these acidic compounds are neutralized or eliminated in some manner, they will continue to damage the already weakened fibers and, in time, reduce the document to dust particles. Besides this injury to the document, further damage may be expected since many of these compounds migrate into the materials used to strengthen and reinforce a deteriorated document, thus causing a premature breakdown of the restored sheet.

## Methods of Deacidification

When it was ascertained that practically all papers needing restoration were highly acid, there was the problem of selecting the most suitable method of eliminating this condition. Soaking the documents in plain water for an hour or more was tried first, but this did not eliminate the acidity entirely, and the papers had a tendency to become more acid during artificial aging. Solutions of sodium bicarbonate were tried also, but they proved to be injurious when used in relatively large concentrations, and again the papers had a tendency to return toward the acid side of the pH scale. These two procedures, therefore, did not prove entirely satisfactory.

The previously mentioned test data of the National Bureau of Standards; Jarrell, Hankins, and Veitch; and Torrey and Sutermeister indicated that calcium compounds had been an important factor in the preservation of several early papers of the seventeenth, eighteenth, and nineteenth centuries. Later, Lewis reported similar findings on papers of the sixteenth century. The data obtained from the above investigations on papers two, three, and four hundred years old are good evidence that calcium carbonate is noninjurious to cellulose fibers and, from all indications, has a beneficial effect on their permanency. These studies pointed the way to the use of calcium compounds in neutralizing the acidity of early documents. Calcium bicarbonate was tried first but difficulties were encountered in consistently getting a solution of sufficient strength to neutralize all of the acids. When several somewhat deteriorated and acid papers were treated with solutions of calcium hydroxide and calcium bicarbonate, I found that there was good retention of folding endurance after artificial aging and there was no particular tendency toward acid renewal. The acid in these specimens was effectively neutralized, and a small amount of calcium carbonate was precipitated in the paper, which gave a pH slightly above 7.0. (For further information on these tests, consult item 4 in the Paper Bibliography.) Comparative results with solutions of calcium bicarbonate alone and calcium hydroxide followed by the calcium bicarbonate were recently reported by the Swedish National Testing Laboratory to Dr. Ingvar Andersson, the National Archivist of Sweden. At present, Mr. Erick Grill, of Riksarkivet, is preparing the results of these tests for publication.

In addition to the studies of early papers, the recent investigation of Shaw and O'Leary indicated that calcium carbonate used as a filler in low-grade papers has a protective effect when these papers are artificially aged. Mr. A. R. R. Westman, of the Ontario Research Foundation, has concurred in similar findings in his study of the use of alkali earth metal carbonates in making a certain type of wrapping paper. It has been known for years that the carbonates and bicarbonates of calcium interfere with many chemical reactions, and they have been often classified as inhibitors. Since calcium carbonate has this characteristic, it is not surprising to find that it has an inhibiting effect on many compounds causing deterioration in the cellulose fiber. In addition to this protective influence, the small amount precipitated during deacidification will also prevent, up to a point, the paper's becoming acidic from adverse storage conditions.

When the two calcium solutions are used to neutralize the acid in a document, the sheet is placed first between specially constructed, woven-wire cloth and is submerged for about 20 minutes in a solution of lime water which is approximately 0.15 percent calcium hydroxide. This solution will effectively neutralize the amount of acid usually found in a document. It is then transferred for another 20 minutes to a solution of approximately 0.15 percent calcium bicarbonate. The calcium bicarbonate will carbonate the calcium hydroxide left in the paper from the first solution and will precipitate calcium carbonate in the fibers of the paper. The document is then air-dried, and any calcium bicarbonate in the paper breaks down into calcium carbonate and carbon dioxide. To some custodians the concentration of these solutions may seem somewhat low, but the amount of acid in deteriorated paper is likewise small although quite damaging to cellulose fibers over a long period of time.

The writing inks made of carbon, Prussian blue, and other particles which are held to the paper with gum arabic are often easily smudged while wet and care must be exercised when handling them in this condition. If much difficulty is anticipated with such writing, sponging the document with the calcium solutions usually overcomes this problem. It is only occasionally that such problems occur among documents written from 1400 to 1850. Due to the nature of their binders, the early printing inks do not run or smudge.

It is of interest to note that red ink made of brazilwood is water-soluble when first made, but the writings made with this ink become relatively insoluble after approximately one hundred to one hundred and fifty years. There is some indication that in time this may happen to writings made of the coal-tar dyestuff, which was discovered in 1856. There is no improvement in the color of brazilwood writing after deacidification and sometimes there is a small loss in tone. Dusting a document with calcium carbonate rather than using the regular procedure will eliminate any possibility of the ink's running. This is not as effective as the solutions but is better than no attempt to neutralize the acid at all. Since acidic compounds are somewhat migratory, it is thought that as time passes most of the acidity will be neutralized by this dusting process.

## Characteristics of a Deacidified Document

Badly discolored papers often lose some of this property during deacidification. Otherwise, relatively little or no change can be observed in a document after treatment. Since most of the writings made between 1400 and 1850 are of iron gall inks, it seemed advisable to me to carefully check the effects of the solutions on this type of ink. One hundred and fifteen small specimens of the sixteenth through nineteenth centuries were selected, and each was cut through the writing into two parts. One half of each specimen was deacidified with the calcium solutions and the two halves were examined later, visually and under magnification. The black writings exhibited no change in color. When first examined, some of the rusty brown writings appeared slightly less dense in color, but within two weeks most of them had reverted to their original appearance. Heating similar specimens for two minutes at 200° F. produced similar results. There were a few specimens on which the writing continued to appear somewhat less dense in color. This occurred only when the paper had whitened and there was a light deposit of rusty brown ink. An examination of the writing under magnification revealed no indication of change in color of the ink particles. Mr. Berkeley Williams, Jr., artist, of Richmond, Virginia, called my attention to the fact that this ink was somewhat transparent and its whiter background of paper fibers was a factor which caused the ink stroke to appear lighter in color. Another factor contributing to this change which he mentioned was that the area interspersed among the ink particles in the pen stroke was also whitened. It was concluded that this change was due primarily to the change in the color of the paper. This conclusion later appeared to be correct, as no particular change could be noted in the treated specimens at the end of six months, as the paper had reverted to approximately its original color. These observations indicate that specimens treated by this method of deacidification should not be evaluated until a period of six months has elapsed. After a careful examination of all of the specimens at the end of six months, only three or four specimens appeared to be slightly less dense in color, and about the same number of specimens showed an increase in density of color. This change could be attributed to the change in color of the paper. It can be said in general that the deacidified specimens appeared cleaner and slightly better than their untreated counterparts.

A similar experiment was conducted on twenty-five manuscripts written between 1900 and 1920. No change in color was found in the very black writings, but those that were turning brown seemed to have this color change accelerated by the deacidification baths. This seems to confirm my previous statement that black iron inks which turn rusty-brown do so during the first one hundred years, as this changing condition was not noticeable in any of the writings made previous to 1900.

Very interesting results were obtained on two specimens that were purposely exposed to sunlight. There was a decided fading of these faint brown writings after deacidification, but a color slightly better than before deacidification was observed within two weeks. A similar result was obtained on four documents sent to my shop for restoration. They had been exposed to light for some time in a frame. After restoration, the color in the writing of the documents appeared to be slightly more dense than before.

In view of the fact that calcium carbonate is considered to have a beneficial effect on the permanency of cellulose fibers, it is difficult to think that the very mild solutions used in this process would have a harmful effect during deacidification. It was thought that there might be a slight change in the structure of the paper due to swelling of the fibers while wet. Eight eighteenth-century papers were selected for testing the comparative values before and after deacidification. Two of these papers showed a loss in folding endurance while the other six showed an increase. The average folding endurance for all eight papers increased 28 percent. These tests indicated that no physical damage was done to the papers by the deacidification process. Since the original strength of these papers was very low, no particular value can be placed on this increase in folding endurance. The folding machine used in making these tests is similar in principle to the M.I.T. tester, but was designed to fold the test specimens only 90 degrees. With this apparatus weak papers can be tested, and these are the types of papers of particular interest in this study.

Since most of the early papers were sized with animal glue, some of the sizing could be expected to soak out during deacidification. While glue is not particularly soluble in cold water, it seemed advisable to investigate its solubility in the calcium solutions. Three eighteenth-century papers were soaked in the calcium solutions for twenty-four hours, and other specimens were soaked for shorter periods of time. Writings made with modern, water-soluble dyes on all of these specimens after drying had no tendency to feather. This test does not prove that there was no loss of glue, but it does indicate that if there were any loss, it was negligible. Since sufficient sizing for good writing remained in the paper, the amount needed for physical properties may also be considered sufficient for all practical purposes. No starch sizing was found in the early papers tested, but if it does exist there is no reason to think that it will dissolve out, as it is less soluble than glue.

## Exposure to Light

Light is a potent enemy of paper. Regardless of the custodian's efforts to provide nearly perfect storage conditions for a document, it still must be exposed to light at intervals. The periodic reading of a manuscript necessitates that the sheet be exposed to light, which will add up to many hours over a period of time. Since most reading rooms use natural light, it was deemed advisable to subject several papers for a number of hours to natural sunlight passing through a glass window. Four eighteenth-century papers having a pH of 4.5 to 4.7 were deacidified, and specimens of untreated and treated sheets were exposed for 28 days during April in Richmond, Virginia. This cannot be considered a long time as compared to the length of the exposures used in the experiments of other workers, but in relation to the normal usage of documents it seemed to be an adequate amount of time. The four untreated papers showed an average loss in folding endurance of 22 percent, and the same papers deacidified had an average loss of 7 percent. A longer exposure no doubt would give greater loss in each group, but the deacidification and the calcium carbonate did help the paper to resist some of the harmful effects of light. On modern papers, Launer and Wilson obtained similar findings, as did Richter.

To determine if the calcium carbonate had a harmful or beneficial effect on the iron gall writing, both deacidified and untreated portions of ten documents were exposed to sunlight shining through a window. The specimens consisted of one sheet written during the sixteenth century, two of the seventeenth century, three of the eighteenth century, and four of the nineteenth century. With the exception of two specimens, no change can be noted in the deacidified and untreated portions. The principal change in these two specimens seems to be due to the change in the color of the paper, as but very little change can be noted in the ink particles when examined under magnification. Twenty-two weeks of exposure, however, from March through August, may be considered much more exposure than normally can be expected for the average document over a period of many years. These specimens are still being exposed to sunlight for a future evaluation.

## Problems in Deacidification

Many think that only documents in fair physical condition can be deacidified. This is not the case, for very brittle and deteriorated documents can be deacidified with the use of proper materials and equipment. This point is discussed by J. Bolsée in his article, "La restauration des documents aux Archives Générales du Royaume." It is possible to subject charred papers to calcium solutions provided proper precautions are taken. This applies to other very brittle and weak papers which Alvin W. Kremer, of the Library of Congress, in his article, "The Preservation of Wood Pulp Publications," describes as "fluffing to the four winds."

During deacidification, the tapes with water-soluble adhesives, previously applied for repairs, float off the sheet into the solution. Those tapes with adhesives which are insoluble in water should be removed with their respective solvents before treatment, as the calcium compounds are stabilizing agents and will harden many of the adhesives. Dust particles and pencil marks should likewise be removed as they become somewhat fixed after deacidification. The use of chlorine should be avoided in cleaning manuscripts as it can be damaging to paper and frequently ruinous to iron inks. More research is needed on mending tapes as some exhibit damage to the area of the paper and inks to which they are applied. This is especially true of the cellophane type tape. After a few years, the adhesive gradually becomes darker in color and more insoluble, and no solvent has been found which will remove it at an advanced stage of decomposition. The paper fibers and adhesive, after some years, become a black, hard, and brittle mass that falls from the remainder of the sheet.

## Summary

Since an injurious amount of acid is found in nearly all deteriorated papers, it is necessary to neutralize this acidity if the document is to have a good degree of permanency. It is realized that there are other causes of deterioration besides acidity, but the results of this entire study indicate that acidity is the primary cause, and the compounds producing this condition are the principal injurious ones left in the deteriorated papers of 1400 to 1850. The use of calcium hydroxide and calcium bicarbonate appears to be the most effective and suitable method so far devised for eliminating this acidity. A small amount of calcium carbonate is precipitated in the paper which has a stabilizing effect when the paper is subjected to light and to accelerated aging. No ill effect on the papers has been found after soaking them in the calcium solutions. In most cases, the solutions have no effect on the color of the writings made of iron gall inks. When a change does occur, it is only temporary, as the writing reverts to its original color within six months. Care must be exercised to prevent smudging of other inks composed of gum arabic and an insoluble pigment. Printing inks have exhibited no tendency to run or smudge. No particular difficulties have been encountered in the practical application of this process, but it should be called to the attention of the reader that, as stated in chapter 1, no attempt should be made to carry out these procedures without first receiving proper instructions, or after a long period of experimentation.

# VI The Lamination of Documents

In 1936, my attention was called to cracks in the leaves of two record books which had been restored by the silk or crepelene process several years earlier. Upon a careful examination, it was found that these leaves were quite brittle and the silk had become discolored. Such irregularities appeared less frequently on other similarly treated volumes which were examined, but the silk muslin on these leaves had been applied more recently. The deterioration of this cloth in these two volumes caused me considerable concern, as I was using this procedure of restoration at that time. As a result of this investigation, it was obvious that better and more lasting methods were needed for the restoration of deteriorated documents.

## Investigation of Lamination

In the early 1930s, cellulose acetate film was laminated to new, printed material to protect the surface of a sheet and to impart a unique effect for display purposes. This process consists of heating the film to a plastic condition and pressing a small portion of it into the pores of the paper. The depth of its penetration for good adhesion is about one-eighth of the thickness of average weight paper. After the application of heat and pressure and after the sheet has been cooled, the film is securely molded to the paper. Lamination with cellulose acetate film gives protection to a deteriorated document, and it increases the physical strength of the sheet to a limited extent. This type of lamination requires special, precision-built apparatus and cannot be done with inexpensive equipment.

According to the recent studies of William Haynes, cellulose acetate was first prepared in 1869 by Schutzenberger and Naudin of France, but due to manufacturing difficulties, it was not made into film on a large scale until about 1930. The New York Public Library was the first institution, to my knowledge, to try the lamination of this film to the leaves of a volume as a means of restoration. The method employed by the commercial concern that did this lamination was the same as the process described above.

When an investigation of other methods of restoration was made, it was found that the Paper Section of the National Bureau of Standards was then completing a special research program on the lamination of documents with cellulose acetate film. The results of this research on .0088-inch-thick film demonstrated that such film was well suited for document restoration as it had good stability on artificial aging, relatively good flexibility, nonabsorbency, and resistance to microorganisms, insects, and passage of gases. Its transparency permits the passage of ultraviolet, infrared, and other rays and is, therefore, no bar to photography. One of the undesirable properties is the increased weight of the sheet after lamination, but this has not proven to be a problem of much consequence. After the research at the National Bureau of Standards indicated that this film had good stability, its adoption gradually became general in the archival and library fields.

If cellulose acetate film is made under proper conditions and with appropriate plasticizers, it has a high degree of permanency as ascertained by the artificial aging test. When subjected to other tests for permanency, it exhibits properties similar to the best grades of rag papers. There are a number of cellulose acetate films on the market today, and care must be exercised in selecting one with a good, stable plasticizer. Among those generally considered to have good stability and to be satisfactory for this purpose are dimethoxy ethyl phthalate, diethyl phthalate, and triphenyl phosphate. Since the early investigation of films at the National Bureau of Standards was made, many other plasticizers have been developed. This creates a need for improved procedures for testing the permanency of the various films now on the market. At the present time, the Paper Section of the National Bureau of Standards is making a study of this nature.

In 1937, when cellulose acetate film was first applied to documents in my shop, it was realized that due to the limited tear resistance of this film the document would not withstand normal usage. Since the tear resistance of deteriorated documents already is very low, an increase in this property is needed if they are to acquire adequate *durability*. Later, the test data in *Protection of Documents with Cellulose Acetate Sheeting*, by B. W. Scribner, and experiments that I made, showed that the resistance to tearing of some papers is slightly reduced by the addition of this film. It was obvious, therefore, that some other material with good tear resistance should be incorporated in the laminate to give this necessary property. For this purpose, a high quality tissue was selected as it not only increases the tear resistance, but also increases the folding endurance. In addition, it helps to impart a finish on the surface of the restored document not unlike the original paper. The recent articles of Bolsée and Kremer recommend the use of tissue in lamination of documents receiving normal or frequent usage. Charles Braibant, Archivist of France, also advocates the use of tissue in his publication, *Archives* (Numéro spécial de l'education nationale). An examination of papers so laminated during the past seventeen years demonstrated that this evaluation was correct.

To insure permanency, the fibers of tissue used in lamination should have the same chemical purity as those used in making the best and most lasting rag papers. There should be evenness in texture, or the visibility of the text in some areas of a restored document may be marred. The diameter of the fiber and the thickness of the sheet (weight per ream) are factors in visibility and tear resistance. Tear resistance should not be sacrificed for high visibility, and vice versa. I have found that a 6½-pound tissue, size 24 x 36 inches, with large fibers, is satisfactory for the average document with good, legible writing. Documents containing faint writing should have a thinner tissue, and one of 5½ pounds, size 24 x 36 inches, with fibers of a smaller diameter, is more suitable for maximum visibility. It should be noted that this 5½-pound tissue has much less tear resistance than the 6½-pound tissue. This is a factor of much importance for documents frequently handled. Only occasionally do I find writing so faint that it necessitates and, I think, justifies the use of lightweight tissue.

## Lamination of a Document

The application of cellulose acetate film and tissue to a document follows the deacidification process. H. M. Nixon, of the British Museum, in his article, "Lamination of Paper Documents with Cellulose Acetate Foil," gives a good description of the order in which these materials are laid out so as to form a sandwich. It is as follows:

tissue
film
document
film
tissue

The thermoplastic cellulose acetate film in this sandwich softens under heat and can be pressed into the pores of the paper and tissue to form a homogeneous unit. The amount of heat and pressure needed varies with the porosity of the paper, but the approximate temperature range is from 315° F. to 320° F., and the pressure over 700 pounds per square inch. These estimates are based on a short cycle, which requires only 35 seconds for the complete operation. The application of this film should be made only with a precision-built piece of apparatus, which controls very accurately the heat and pressure. With the proper equipment and an intelligent operator, good results are easily obtained, but the reverse may be expected with either an incompetent operator or poor equipment.

## Physical Properties of a Laminated Sheet

The physical strength of weak papers is increased considerably by lamination with cellulose acetate and tissue. For instance, the folding endurance of newly made newsprint increases twelve times, and the tear resistance, four times. When laminated, a deteriorated paper increases in strength many times, but this added strength cannot be considered as great as that of the strongest grades of rag paper nor as small as the low-grade papers. Careful handling, proper storage, and such additions as binding margins are factors which help assure even longer usage.

An important factor in retaining the physical strength of a restored sheet and preserving the original document is the addition of highly stable materials and the elimination of those impurities which have caused deterioration within the document. The test data on five eighteenth-century papers, which I reported in the July 1943 issue of *The American Archivist*, illustrate this point. Those papers deacidified and laminated with cellulose acetate film and tissue lost an average of only five percent in folding endurance after artificial aging, while the same papers which were laminated after no deacidification with only the film lost thirty-one percent. Even though good stable materials were used in the lamination of all of these papers, the impurities left in the original paper continued to have an adverse effect.

Additional information in this respect was obtained recently by testing six somewhat deteriorated papers made in the seventeenth, eighteenth, and nineteenth centuries. In order to have specimens similar in composition to an original manuscript, inked lines were drawn in the proportion of one inked space to seven uninked spaces. This was estimated to be about the proportion found in many early manuscripts. The iron gall ink used was composed of 6.0 grams of ferrous sulfate, 4.68 grams tannic acid, 1.52 grams gallic acid, 3.0 grams gum arabic, and 100 c.c. distilled water. This formula is somewhat less concentrated than the average of the formulae found in table 1. The pH of the specimens before and after inking may be found in table 3.

Table 3 Folding endurance of laminated sheets

| | | | | % retention of folding endurance after inking and heating 72 hours at 100° C. | | |
|---|---|---|---|---|---|---|
| Sample no. | Date paper made | pH of paper | pH after inking | Paper not laminated | Laminated & delaminated after aging | Deacidified, laminated & delaminated after aging |
| 1 | 1694 | 4.7 | 4.5 | 70 | 40* | 98 |
| 2 | 1710 | 4.8 | 4.6 | 85 | 71* | 105 |
| 3 | 1764 | 4.6 | 4.4 | 73* | 49* | 103 |
| 4 | 1799 | 4.7 | 4.4 | 68 | 69* | 127 |
| 5 | 1820 | 4.8 | 4.5 | 60 | 84* | 92 |
| 6 | 1840 | 5.0 | 4.7 | 50 | 78 | 121 |

* Slight discoloration after artificial aging.

Three samples of each paper were prepared for artificial aging, which consisted of heating for 72 hours at 100° C. The first sample was not laminated, the second was laminated, and the third was deacidified and laminated in the manner prescribed in this publication. After aging, the laminated specimens were delaminated by soaking for 45 minutes in each of three fresh solutions of acetone. The folding endurance test was made on all samples to note any embrittlement caused by the acidity during the aging process. The results may be found in table 3.

Since the loss in folding endurance of the unlaminated sheets averaged about the same as those laminated without deacidification, it can be concluded from the test data that the acids in these papers continued to be active even though laminated. On the other hand, when these same inked papers were deacidified and laminated, there was no general loss in folds after artificial aging. It may be concluded from these tests that the deacidification checks deterioration within the papers and the principal value of lamination is to add physical strength to the document and prevent the absorption of impurities.

## Binding Margins and Inlays

Laminated documents, as well as those treated by the silk or tissue processes, should not be folded or subjected to very sharp bends, as under frequent use they will break prematurely. The stresses set up on the outside curve of such a bend are beyond the point of elasticity of either silk, tissue, or cellulose acetate film. In the case of books, booklets, etc., a binding margin made of either tissue, bond paper, or cloth has been used for a number of years on all types of restoration. This margin should always be slightly more flexible than the restored sheet. As a result of this addition, a laminated leaf bound into a volume can be turned with almost no stress on the old paper. On the other hand, if the binding margin is less flexible or stiffer than the old sheet, after some usage a break can be expected to occur where the old sheet and the margin join. This is a very important point in any type of restoration. Skilled craftsmen acquire the art of creating a margin with the right flexibility through proper training and experience. The thickness and width of a margin naturally must vary with the flexibility and width of the old sheet. I have found a 9-pound paper (9 pounds per 500 sheets, size 17 by 22 inches) to be satisfactory for most leaves ten inches or less in width, and a 13-pound paper for those which are wider. Of course, the paper used for binding margins should conform to the standards for permanency.

The three basic functions of a binding margin are: first, to reduce wear on the original sheet; second, to provide new materials for sewing the volume; and third, to place writing on the inner margin of the restored leaf in a position of better visibility. A similar margin serves a useful purpose in making into a booklet a small group of manuscripts that are considered a complete unit. Through these margins, the manuscripts can be sewed into a file folder or coverboard which affords protection to the sheets and prevents them from slipping out of the folder and becoming damaged.

Besides the addition of a binding margin, worm holes or missing portions of the paper are filled in either with paper or additional sheets of cellulose acetate and tissue. The nature of the document determines the type of material used. These inlays of new material give an even structual balance to the sheet. This is especially important in books, as otherwise a leaf, when turned, will sag, thus placing most of the stress on the area which is missing in the sheet and eventually causing a premature failure at this point. The inlay has proved to be of value in the earlier methods of restoration, and this is also true of lamination.

## Letter-Press Copies

Thin papers, such as those used in making letter-press copies, seldom have sufficient rigidity or tear resistance to withstand constant usage. Mounting them on a strong rag paper by lamination increases the physical strength to the extent that they then may be handled as any ordinary sheet. If the legibility of a letter-press copy is poor, it is often improved by omitting the tissue on the face of the document as the cellulose actetate film slightly increases the transparency of the copy sheet. This gives better visibility to the ink which in many cases has migrated only part of the way through the paper. The readability of a letter-press copy is thus improved by increased visibility of the ink and the addition of a relatively white opaque background. Since the early letter-press copies were made with iron gall ink, it is quite necessary that they be deacidified before lamination. The principle in making these copies consisted of dampening the original soon after it was written, and causing rapid migration under pressure of some of the soluble unoxidized iron gall ink to the copy sheet. Some of the sulfuric acid in the original writing also migrated during this procedure, and while this was an unfortunate addition for the copy, it did decrease the acidity of the original.

## Maps

The deacidification of early hand-drawn maps requires the same consideration as manuscripts, due to the nature of their inks. The removal of dust particles, unwanted pencil marks, and so forth, should be made previous to acid neutralization for reasons already explained. Printed maps made before 1850 offer no problems due to the types of pigments and binders used in the inks. A few of the colored inks used in more recent printing occasionally feather to a limited extent on account of the addition of water-soluble dyes. Sponging with calcium solutions usually overcomes this problem.

The restoration of deteriorated early maps follows a pattern similar to the lamination of documents. As a rule, the tissue is omitted from the face of the map and a piece of cloth is substituted for the sheet of tissue usually placed on the reverse side. The completed sandwich is as follows:

cellulose acetate film
map
cellulose acetate film
cloth

The lamination of these materials is effected by the application of heat and pressure as described before.

The type of cloth generally used is a high-grade cotton muslin which is considered to have a good degree of permanency. When there is a limited amount of writing on the reverse side of a map, a very thin, coarsely woven cloth is used instead of a heavier one. If there is much small writing or print on this reverse side, then it may be necessary to use only the acetate film and tissue on each side. This latter procedure does not, as a rule, give sufficient strength for a large sheet receiving hard use. Of course, a laminated sheet can be split and the two halves mounted on cloth by lamination, but this increases the labor cost and slightly alters the appearance of an old map when examined closely. This is a problem which occurs only occasionally.

As a rule, maps and many broadsides are much larger in size than the average document. In use, large sheets are often subjected to stresses beyond the limits of their resistance to tear, and for this reason mounting maps on cloth has been practiced for years. This mounting is often done to prevent injury to frequently used modern maps, and may be considered the exception to the previously mentioned rule of not attempting preservative methods unless the sheet exhibits some form of deterioration. Until recently, all map mounting was accomplished by either pasting or gluing the map to cotton or linen cloth. Institutions having large collections of modern maps now find it much more economical to mount them on cloth by lamination with cellulose acetate film. If the proper thickness of cloth is used, the necessary rigidity, flexibility, and tear resistance is obtained. When a sheet of cellulose acetate film is laminated to the face of a map, it will prevent ink spots, pencil marks, etc. from disfiguring or altering the text. At times, the latter can be a factor of considerable importance if copies are made by photographic processes.

## Charred Documents

Papers which have been charred black, but not reduced to grey ash, can be laminated. Older methods have not proven satisfactory for most charred material. It is advisable to laminate with only cellulose acetate film even though this limits the durability of the document. The elimination of the tissue facilitates photography of the obscured writings made of iron gall inks. After a copy is made for research purposes, the original is generally placed in dead storage due to its limited strength and the low visibility of the writing. A small improvement in the legibility of the writings made of iron inks sometimes can be observed after lamination.

A small amount of cellulose acetate film dissolved in acetone and applied to the document with either a spray or a brush is helpful in that it softens and slightly strengthens the sheet previous to lamination. The addition of a small amount of plasticizer to the solution increases this softening effect. To flatten a cockled sheet after the application of this solution takes from a few days to a few weeks. Charred documents can be deacidified, but the use of proper equipment in conveying the sheet into and out of the solutions is essential. No investigation has been made on the pH of charred documents, but the results of such a study would be of interest and value. Although no great difficulties have been encountered in the actual lamination of charred papers, they require considerably more time and care in handling than ordinary documents of a less brittle nature. However, the preparation of a charred sheet for lamination sometimes presents very difficult problems and is a challenge to one's skill.

The studies conducted by Raymond Davis, photographic technologist of the National Bureau of Standards, in regard to making copies of charred documents by placing them in contact with photographic film for a number of days give very interesting results. The procedure takes advantage of migrating compounds within the charred sheet which react with the film to produce results similar to ordinary exposure. The ink blocks this action in the area on which it is deposited, and therefore, the film when developed will have white writing on a dark background.

## Storage

It is important that restored material be stored flat, and not rolled or folded. Oversize containers are recommended for extra-large sheets. Occasionally, when conditions justify it, large sheets are sectioned and the sections are either filed or bound as separate sheets. Another procedure is to join the sections together with lightweight bond paper, similar to a binding margin, making a fold in the new material. In addition to proper containers, temperature, humidity, light rays, polluted air, insects, rodents, etc. are all factors which the custodian must study in order to provide satisfactory storage conditions for his records.

File folders, end sheets, interleaving sheets, book markers, coverboards, or any other type of material in contact with the document should be free of acidity, groundwood fibers, or other compounds injurious to paper. These impurities often migrate into the document and cause deterioration and discoloration. For further information on this subject, it is suggested that items 3 and 84 in the Paper Bibliography be consulted. The latter article, which is written by W. J. Van Schreeven, Virginia state archivist, gives other helpful information on storage containers.

To prevent this potential damage to valuable records, it is recommended that all of the above types of materials be subjected to laboratory tests. They should be free of groundwood fibers and have a pH of not less than 5.0. An aging test of 72 hours at 100° C. with a loss of not more than 25 percent folding endurance is also desirable. These tests should conform to accepted standard testing methods.

## Delamination

There is always the possibility that a restored document may become torn or otherwise damaged and will require the removal of the materials used to strengthen it. Sometimes a missing portion of a document is found after the restoration of the principal body of the sheet, which necessitates rerestoration. The value of being able to rerestore is properly stressed in the writings of Sir Hiliary Jenkinson, deputy keeper of the Public Record Office in London. A laminated document can be delaminated and relaminated after soaking in a bath of acetone. Cellulose acetate film is readily soluble in acetone, and it requires relatively little labor to perform this operation of delamination.

## Effect of Pressure during Lamination

The advisability of applying high pressure to a deteriorated paper is sometimes questioned by those who are not familiar with the characteristics of paper. Unless there is an even distribution of pressure during lamination, damage can be done. This is one of the reasons for recommending only equipment which has been built with a high degree of accuracy. This factor has been recognized by paper manufacturers for a number of years, as very high pressures are exerted on papers when they are calendered. Microscopic examination does not reveal any injury to the fibers of brittle papers when subjected to pressures needed for laminating. It is a daily occurrence in restoration shops to laminate papers so brittle that they can be reduced to dust if rubbed between the fingers. When properly flattened and prepared for lamination, even charred papers can be processed with satisfactory results. S. Chakravorti, in his article "A Review of the Lamination Process," reports that among some less brittle paper, there is a slight increase in folding endurance after the application of the pressure needed during lamination. Tests that I made of four eighteenth-century papers indicated that there was an average increase of 7 percent in folding endurance after the papers had been subjected to deacidification and the usual heat and pressure required during lamination.

## Effects of Very High Temperatures and Flame

There has been some speculation regarding the salvage possibilities if a laminated book were subjected to high temperatures during a fire.

Cellulose acetate film burns nearly as fast as paper, and it would not inhibit damage by flame. If the leaves of a book were laminated with tissue, as previously recommended, they would not likely weld or fuse together unless high pressure were simultaneously exerted on the volume. However, the reverse will occur with sheets laminated without tissue, as little or no pressure is needed for this film to fuse when heated to high temperatures. In the tests conducted by the Swedish National Testing Laboratory, the data obtained after heating the laminated sheet to nearly the point of charring indicated that the papers could still be delaminated with acetone. I know of no one who has had actual experience in salvaging laminated records damaged by fire, and my estimates are based only upon laboratory data. Recently, I attempted to separate two silked documents whose edges had become welded together during a fire. Various procedures in addition to soaking the sheets in water for a long period of time failed to soften the starch adhesive in the general area of the charred edges. From this experience, I have concluded that a volume laminated with tissue would have equal or better salvage possibilities after a fire than would one restored by silk.

## Films Containing Adhesives

Cellulose acetate films containing adhesives first appeared on the market in the late 1930s. These adhesives have proved to be unstable, and the film usually peels off the document within a very few years, leaving the adhesive embedded in the pores of the paper. The instability of many of these adhesives is such that they must be used within two months after their manufacture as otherwise they harden into an unusable condition. Deteriorated documents treated in this manner become torn easily due to the limited tear resistance of the film. While this film serves a useful purpose for the protection of menu cards, inexpensive book covers, etc., it should not be used on documents of permanent value.

## Lamination with Cellulose Acetate Film Alone

The restoration of deteriorated documents by lamination with only the cellulose acetate film and omitting deacidification and the use of tissue has been adopted by relatively few institutions. Documents treated by this procedure often exhibit tears after some use. This could be expected, as test data obtained when the process first came into use indicated a very low resistance to tearing. It also provides limited folding endurance when compared with sheets laminated with the addition of tissue. One of the most important factors, however, is its failure to eliminate those compounds which cause deterioration within the paper fibers. While this method of lamination gives a number of desirable properties to a deteriorated sheet, it does not provide the *durability* and *permanency* essential for documents of historical value.

## Summary

The lamination of deteriorated documents with cellulose acetate film and tissue produces a sheet with moderate physical strength when compared with modern papers. In the case of bound volumes, additional wear can be obtained by the use of new binding margins, which must be more flexible than the old leaf. Test data indicate that the laminate has good lasting qualities provided it has been deacidified and laminated with stable materials. Letter-press copies, charred documents, maps, etc. can also be laminated. Maps are mounted on cloth by lamination to give results superior to older methods. Cellulose acetate films containing adhesives are not suitable for document restoration due to the instability of the adhesives. Deteriorated documents laminated with only the film and no deacidification have limited durability and permanency. Documents can be delaminated with acetone and relaminated in the usual manner. There has been no indication that the pressure and temperature used in the process have been injurious to the deteriorated fibers of paper if they are properly applied. Test data indicate that possibilities of salvage after a fire are as good as or better than with older methods of restoration. This conclusion is based on those documents laminated with tissue, which is the generally recommended procedure.

# VII Conclusions of This Study

During the past few decades, the principal methods used in the restoration of deteriorated documents have been the silk process, the tissue process, lamination with only cellulose acetate film, and the deacidification of the document, followed by lamination with cellulose acetate film and tissue. The cloth used in the silk process has not proven to be a stable material and documents treated by this process generally have to be restored again within twenty to thirty years. The tissue process produces a sheet quite low in both visibility and strength. Documents laminated with only cellulose acetate film have very limited tear resistance and do not hold up well under frequent usage. None of these three processes eliminates the acidity generally found in a deteriorated sheet. This acidity not only continues to weaken the old fibers but, in many instances, it migrates to the reinforcing material and does further damage. These processes lack either *durability*, *permanency*, or good *legibility*, all of which are considered necessary properties for a restored document.

The process offering the best possibilities is the previously discussed procedure of deacidification and lamination with cellulose acetate film and tissue. Laboratory tests indicate that satisfactory results can be expected if these procedures are properly executed and good stable reinforcing materials are used. While laboratory tests are good indications of what may be expected of a product, time and usage are the ideal ways for testing any process. It was for this reason that a survey was made and tests were conducted on papers that were restored by this process some twelve to seventeen years ago. The restored documents were examined for discoloration, tears, and any evidence of embrittlement. Additional information was obtained by testing several sheets restored in 1939 and some unused cellulose acetate film manufactured in 1940. Any embrittlement of the materials that may have occurred over a period of time can be measured many times more accurately by testing procedures than by visual examination.

## Survey of Restored Documents

Several hundred tax books, which contain about thirty pages each and were restored for the Virginia State Library in 1939 and 1940, have recently been examined. They were found to be in good condition after an estimated usage of one thousand times. In some instances, the covers had been replaced due to the constant wear from handling. Other documents, restored from 1940 to 1945, were also examined and found to be in good condition. One printed volume restored about twelve years ago appeared to have many more years of wear after already having been consulted approximately five thousand times. The above estimates were made by the custodians who serve this material to the public and who have a good idea of its usage. Other volumes which were restored some years ago for other institutions have also been examined and found to be in a satisfactory condition.

Very little of this material was larger than 11 by 18 inches. It is doubtful whether larger sheets will stand as much hard wear, since this condition also exists among books which have not been restored. In this survey two sheets 12 inches wide and from 3 to 4 feet long were found to have tears after considerable usage. Besides the excessive size of these leaves, they were improperly bound, and this seemed to be the principal reason for their tearing. In 1938 and 1940 a few volumes were restored according to the custodian's specifications, which required an extra sheet of cellulose acetate film besides the generally used one sheet of cellulose acetate film and tissue on each side. These leaves are quite heavy and have caused considerable strain on the bindings. Since all laminated sheets are heavier than unlaminated ones, books restored by this method should have extra reinforcement along the spine. Very large and thick volumes should be bound in two parts to obtain optimum wear of the binding and also make them easier to handle.

It is of interest to note that those documents restored after deacidification was developed appeared cleaner and the writing clearer than the ones laminated earlier without deacidification. There was no apparent change in the ink as a result of deacidification or lamination. Two manuscripts of the eighteenth century, which had one half of each sheet deacidified in 1941 by the procedures previously described, exhibited no change in color of the writing when compared with their counterparts which were not treated. Nor was there evidence of embrittlement or discoloration of the cellulose acetate film used in restoring the documents. After some use, laminated documents appear to have slightly better flexibility than those recently laminated. There was a noticeable improvement in binding margins made of thin bond papers over the earlier ones made of tissue.

## Tests of Early Laminated Sheets and Films

Even though there was no visible evidence of embrittlement in the cellulose acetate film after ten to fifteen years of use, there was still a possibility of some loss in physical strength not detectable by the eye. B. W. Scribner found in his study, *Comparison of Accelerated Aging of Record Papers with Normal Aging for Eight Years*, that papers of low and medium stability showed a decided loss in folding endurance and other properties after eight years of natural aging. Jarrell, Hankins, and Veitch likewise recorded similar findings on bond and ledger papers after five and eighteen years of natural aging. Since this condition is generally found among papers and some plastics of known limited stability, it seemed advisable to test some of the early laminated sheets and films.

Seven eighteenth-century sheets which were laminated in 1939 were available for testing. These were sectioned, and half of each sheet was delaminated by soaking for 45 minutes in each of three separate solutions of fresh acetone. The delaminated sheets were relaminated with new cellulose acetate film of the same thickness. Five of these specimens contained tissue, and the same tissue was used again in the relamination. The size of the specimens was small and an average of only seven strips in each direction could be obtained for the fold test instead of the usual ten strips. Two of the samples showed a loss of 26 percent and 32 percent of their folding endurance when compared with the newly laminated counterparts, and the other five had an increase of 15 percent, 114 percent, 26 percent, 170 percent, and 28 percent. The cause of the high increase in two of these samples is not known definitely, but the migration of a small amount of plasticizer from the film to the paper fibers is a possibility. Also, the swelling of the fibers due to change in temperature and humidity over a period of time could gradually give more space to the fiber in the laminate and thus allow more freedom of action for the fibers when the sheet is manipulated. However, regardless of the cause of the somewhat abnormal results results obtained in two samples, there was no evidence of embrittlement in the cellulose acetate film in these sheets laminated fifteen years ago.

Sheets of cellulose acetate film manufactured in 1940 were also tested to determine if there was a loss in strength during fourteen years of normal aging. This film showed no signs of discoloration, and its laminating properties were as good as new film. Test specimens of four eighteenth-century papers were prepared by laminating one half of each sheet with the film made in 1940 and the other half with film made in 1954. Three of the papers selected registered almost no folds on the folding machine before lamination. When they were laminated, these sheets produced test samples almost entirely dependent upon the film for flexibility and strength. The usual ten strips in each direction of the sheet were tested for folding endurance. One sheet laminated with film made in 1940 had 4 percent fewer folds than that made in 1954, and the other sheets showed an increase of 2 percent, 9 percent, and 20 percent. These tests did not indicate any embrittlement in the cellulose acetate film made in 1940 when compared with that made in 1954.

The data obtained from the survey, the tests of early laminated sheets, and the fourteen-year-old film do not indicate embrittlement or weakening of the cellulose acetate film after normal aging of from twelve to fifteen years. This data supports the evaluation made in the laboratory when cellulose acetate film was first adopted for restoration. This relative evaluation of materials gives cellulose acetate film a good rating at this time since plastic films and papers of low and medium stability generally show a loss in folding endurance during their first ten or fifteen years of natural aging. The reader must be reminded that this film is like paper in that to insure permanency it must be made of stable and proper materials.

Of course, there have been a few instances in which a restored document has been damaged either by accident, improper handling, or unwise planning of its restoration, but as a whole the recommended procedures have produced a product that has given good results. Other repair shops in this country and abroad using these procedures in the restoration of deteriorated documents also report satisfactory results. The documents restored some ten to fifteen years ago appear to be in good shape and will last many more years under good storage conditions and careful handling. The permanency of materials used and the elimination of deteriorative agents within the paper make it a process far superior to older methods of restoration. While the equipment used in this process is more expensive to install than that for the older methods, the total cost per sheet for restoration is much less due to the decrease in labor and the use of less expensive materials.

## Future Developments

During the past few years, good progress has been made in the development of materials and techniques used in document restoration, and it is entirely possible that continued improvement will be made. This can be accomplished more readily if the custodian will work closely with the scientist in well-organized research programs. As more facts are learned about the composition of a deteriorated document and with the development of new plastic films, there will be many possibilities for improvement.

There are several new thermoplastic films on the market which have characteristics not inferior and in some instances superior to the cellulose acetate film. One of these films is myla. However, it softens at a temperature too high for the lamination of documents. Another is polyethylene, which can be easily laminated to paper, but it presents difficulties if delamination is needed as the result of a tear or some other type of accident. Polyethylene is soluble in some solvents such as benzene, but only at a high temperature, which creates a dangerous situation for both the document and the operator. Since delamination is an essential factor in restoration, this film cannot be considered satisfactory for material of historical value. On the other hand, it may prove useful for certain types of material that will be discarded within a limited period of time. There is the possibility that some simpler procedures of delamination may be developed than that already described. It is unfortunate that myla and polyethylene films have these limitations insofar as lamination is concerned, but in time other films will be developed, and some of them may have properties superior to those now available.

Dr. Dorothy M. Schullian, of the Surgeon General's Office, in her article, "Early Print Transfer," describes some interesting procedures of print transfer which were tried in the seventeenth century. The object of these early experiments was to produce an inexpensive second copy of a printed book. Since only one transfer to paper could be made, this necessitated the use of a mirror for reading, as the letters were reversed. The transfer of the print from a deteriorated sheet to new rag paper has been tried in limited quantities during the past few years. This method of preserving the printed text of a book is in the early stages of development and there are many problems yet to be solved. Its potential use lies primarily among reference books printed on low-grade paper some twenty-five to seventy-five years ago. Kremer describes the results to date, and urges an attempt to mechanize the process highly in order to reduce the cost. This is an excellent suggestion, but equipment that performs many complicated operations is expensive to develop. Should such equipment be devised, would there be enough librarians who desire this service to justify such an installation?

Among recent developments of interest is the desilking of documents by converting the insoluble starch adhesive to a soluble sugar with the enzyme Taka-Diastase. More investigation is needed on various details of the process before it can be adopted generally. When more fully explored, this process may be of considerable value, since with the passage of time more silked documents need rerestoration. The present procedures of desilking are slow and remove only part of the hardened starch paste.

There is a possibility that processes may be developed which will strengthen the deteriorated fiber itself. At present, salvaged low-grade papers can be de-inked and the fibers reprocessed and made into a stronger paper. Of course, before this can be considered for documents the de-inking feature must be eliminated. There is also a possibility of the relinkage of the cellulose molecules and the rehabilitation of the fibers' original structure. At present, however, the achievement of such a process seems to lie in the very distant future. There are many other possible developments, but nothing in particular will be gained by enumerating them.

It is unwise for the custodian to wait for the perfect method of restoration and not use the best procedures now available. Should he follow this course, continued deterioration of the weakened fibers takes place, and such papers will be prematurely reduced to dust. It is very true that present procedures do not produce the perfect product which everyone desires. In this respect, a restored document often reminds me of a man who has lost a leg in an accident. By proper treatment, further damage by infection may be prevented and he can be rehabilitated with an artificial limb. It is true that he cannot run races or engage in other types of gymnastics, but he can be returned to society to perform many useful services to mankind. Similarly, a restored document does not have all of the properties of the best record papers, but if the limited properties are taken into consideration, then a sheet restored by the best procedures may be expected to perform valuable functions and last many years.

## Research and Testing

If additional improvements in restoration methods are to be made, continued research and laboratory testing are essential. More information on early ink formulation and papermaking is needed. The reference librarian is not only well qualified to find such information among early studies, but also frequently he can assist in making needed translations of both early and modern treatises. As information of this nature becomes available, the scientist can then determine what compounds should be eliminated from the document and the best procedure for this purpose. The custodian should work closely with the scientist in order that he will properly interpret and understand the data obtained from investigations and tests. Those engaged in restoration can sometimes make valuable suggestions relative to the practical application of proposed methods for restoration. Collaboration between all of these interested parties should exist in the development of procedures for strengthening weakened documents.

In the past, there has been a tendency for the custodian to present the scientist with a particular problem to work out alone. In some instances, the one chosen for the research and testing has never had the opportunity to examine carefully a document of the period involved. Too often he has selected paper of a modern vintage for testing and then evaluated his test data for old papers made in a different period from fibers of another source which were prepared for papermaking under an entirely different process. For instance, in a number of tests modern sulfite and soda papers, which often contain residual chlorine, noncellulose compounds of wood, etc., react differently from old papers whose linen fibers contain residual compounds from bleaching with sour milk and the extract of wood ashes. The old papers now generally receiving restoration were made of rag fibers and prepared by chemical treatment unlike that of most modern papers. In this connection, the custodian in many cases can furnish blank, deteriorating papers of the period for which a given procedure is being designed, and thus make a valuable contribution to the research program.

Writings made with iron gall inks reconstructed by old formulae react differently to certain tests than do the writings made one, two, and three hundred years ago. It has been stated before that most of these writings generally become more inert as time passes. For example, relatively recent writings made of iron gall ink that are gradually turning brown sometimes are affected to a small degree by the deacidification solutions, while the same type of writings a hundred or more years old are relatively unaffected. Again the custodian can be of service by supplying small fragments with writing of the period under study.

Since no laboratory has specialized in the testing of restoration methods, it is quite important that the custodian of records work very closely with the scientist in any type of research program. By such a procedure, the custodian will learn to appreciate the value of experimentation and also understand its limitations. Likewise the scientist can gradually learn more about the characteristics of early documents and the problems confronting the custodian. Many of these problems deal with the practical application of systems and procedures designed in the laboratory. Both custodians and scientists should have a continued interest in such problems, combined with a desire for improvement. It will be through these channels that progress will be made in restoration methods, as there is no prospect for either a simple process that does everything, or a fountain of youth for deteriorated documents.

Custodians should be warned against the overenthusiastic salesman who insists that he has the magic compound that "does everything because it has been tested." The tests conducted may be good or they may be meaningless. Consequently, qualified ink and paper scientists should be consulted regarding new developments before they are applied to documents of value. To assist the custodian in such an investigation, it is suggested that he consider some of the principal factors discussed in this publication.

To summarize, every custodian of valuable documents who makes use of restorative or preservative measures should assure himself that the following details are observed:

1. That all materials used in restoration, including papers, textiles, fibers, films, adhesives, etc., have been tested so as to conform to standards of permanency determined by laboratory experiment.
2. That all procedures used in the restorative process, such as application of heat or pressure, not reduce permanency or impart physical injury.
3. That the restorative measures are not so applied as merely to lock into the treated document those very elements (acid, etc.) which are the causes of its deterioration.
4. That the materials used in restoration will assure the degree of *permanence*, *durability*, and *legibility* required in view of the probable uses of the document.
5. That after restoration the document is kept in such a physical position, and in such freedom from noxious materials or conditions, including contaminated papers or atmosphere, excessive heat, insufficient or excessive humidity, etc., as will assure the permanency and durability which the restorative process has given it.
6. That those craftsmen selected to perform these operations be intelligent, and have manual skill and a good knowledge of the factors entering into the application of the proper restoration procedures.

In conclusion, it may be said that good progress has been made in the last twenty years in the development of sound restoration methods. The custodians of documents who have adopted and encouraged these developments have reported satisfactory results. These improvements have come about through the efforts of many archivists, librarians, scientists, engineers, inventors, machinists, and those engaged in document restoration. Continued improvement can be expected if the custodian will encourage, help, and support these technicians who are able to make many of today's impossibilities become simple realities of tomorrow.

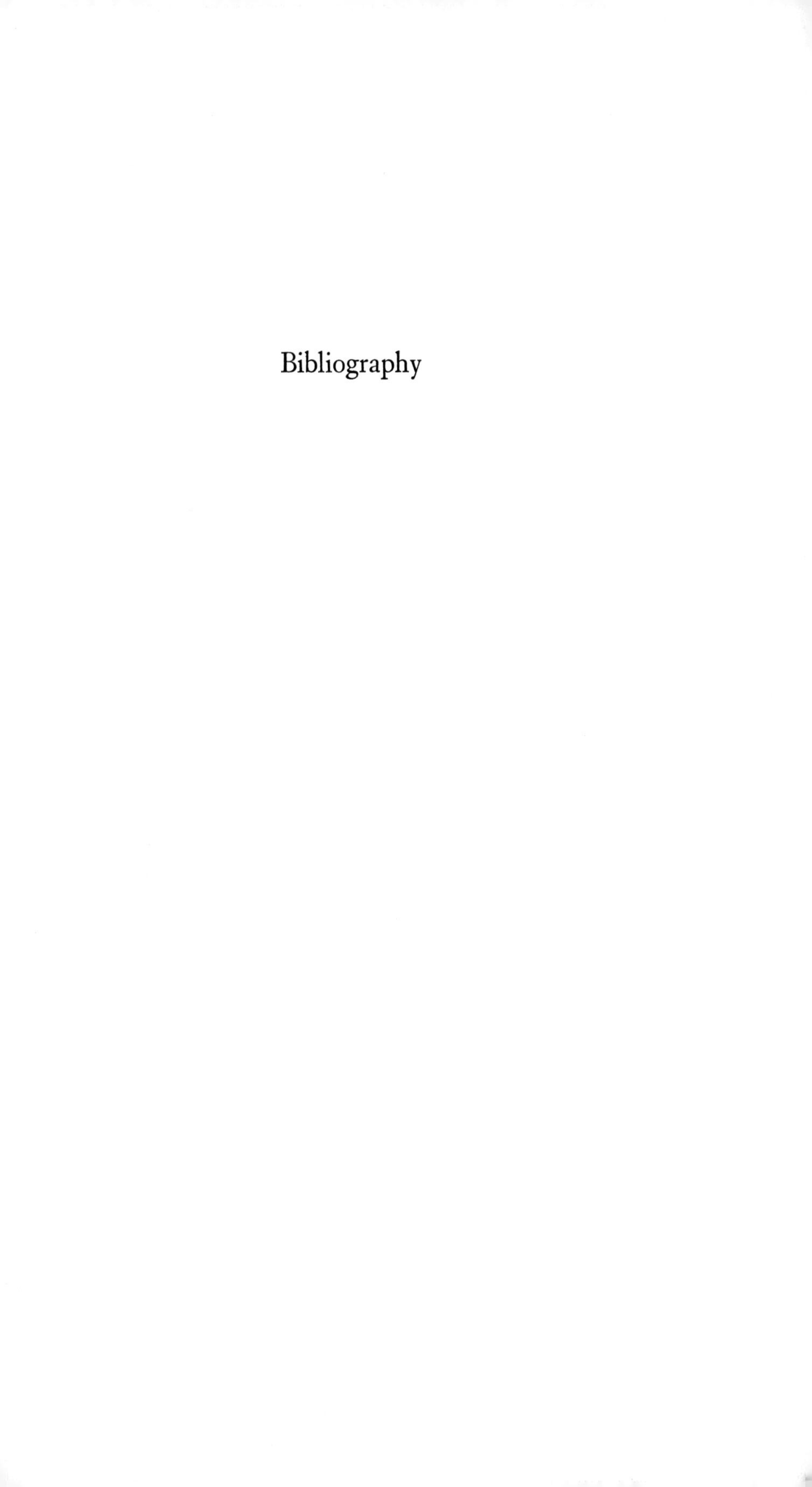

# Bibliography

# Bibliography

## Ink

*Unpublished*


1. Bury St. Edmunds. Bury St. Edmunds and West Suffolk Record Office. Ref. no. N.R.A. 19. [1770–1785]
2. Coventry. City Archives. Memorandum Book of John Whittingham, 1746–1780.
3. Grenoble. Archives of Department of Isère. Minutaire of Sebastien Fabri, 1547.
4. Lancaster. Lancashire Record Office. Document no. DDP: 10/26. [1795]
5. London. Public Record Office. Miscellanea of the Chancery 34/1/3. [1483]
6. Maidstone. Kent Archives Office. Cat. Mark: A.G. H7 (54). [1766]
7. Richmond. Virginia State Library. Norfolk County, Virginia, Wills & Deeds D, 1656–1666. Photostat.
8. Richmond. Virginia State Library. William Allason Letter Book, 1770–1787.
9. Taunton. Somerset Record Office. C/344a DD/SD. [1700]


*Published*


10. Aikin, Arthur, and Charles R. Aikin. *Dictionary of Chemistry and Mineralogy.* 2 vols. London: J. and A. Arch, 1807.
11. [Barrow, John.] *Dictionarium Polygraphicum.* 2 vols. London: C. Hitch and C. Davis, 1735. 2 v.
12. Barrow, William J. "Black Writing Ink of the Colonial Period." *The American Archivist,* XI (October, 1948), 291–307.
13. Bate, John. *The Mysteryes of Nature and Art.* London, 1634.
14. Beauchesne, Jean de. *A Booke Containing Divers Sortes of Hands.* London: T. Vautrouillier, 1571.
15. Caneparius, Pietrus Maria. *De Atramentis Cujuscunque Generis.* 1619. Reprint. London: Joseph Martin, 1660.
16. Carvalho, David N. *Forty Centuries of Ink.* New York: The Banks Law Publishing Co., 1904.
17. Celsus, Aulus Cornelius, *De medicinia.* 3 vols. Loeb Classical Library. Cambridge, Mass.: Harvard University Press, 1935–38.
18. Colwall, Daniel. "An Account of the Way of Making English Green-Copperas." *Philosophical Transactions of the Royal Society of London,* XII (1678), 1056–59.

19. *Cyclopedia; or, Universal Dictionary of Arts, Sciences, and Literature, The.* Edited by Abraham Rees. 41 vols. Philadelphia: S. F. Bradford, 1810–24.
20. Dioscorides, Pedanius. *The Greek Herbal of Dioscorides.* Translated by John Goodyer. Edited by Robert T. Gunther. Oxford: Printed for the author at the University Press, 1934.
21. [Dossie, Robert.] *The Handmaid to the Arts.* 2d ed. 2 vols. London: J. Nourse, 1764.
22. *Encyclopaedia; or, A Dictionary of Arts, Sciences, and Miscellaneous Literature.* 18 vols. Philadelphia: Thomas Dobson, 1790–1797.
23. *Encyclopédie, ou dictionnaire raisonné des sciences, des arts, et des métiers.* Edited by Denis Diderot and Jean le Rond d'Alembert. 17 vols. Paris: Briasson, 1751–65. 2d ed. 36 vols. Geneva: Pellet, 1777–79.
24. Fisher, George. *The Instructor; or, American Young Man's Best Companion.* Philadelphia: John Bioren, 1801.
25. Gallo, Alfonso. *Patologia e terapia del libro.* Rome: Editrice Raggio, 1951.
26. Gode, P. K. "Recipes for Hair-Dyes in the Naranitaka (c. 2nd Century A.D.) and Their Close Affinity with the Recipes for Ink-Manufacture (after A.D. 1000)." *Bharatiya Vidya,* XI (1950).
27. Gode, P. K. "Studies in the History of Indian Palaeography: Some Notes on the History of Ink Manufacture in Ancient and Medieval India and Other Countries." *Praeyavani,* III (October, 1946).
28. *Grosses Vollständiges Universal Lexicon aller Wissenschaften und Kunste.* 64 vols. Halle and Leipzig: Verlegts Johann Heinrich Zedler, 1732–50.
29. Kantrowitz, Morris S., and Earl J. Gosnell. *Alkaline Writing Ink.* U.S. Government Printing Office, Technical Bulletin no. 25, Washington, D.C.: Government Printing Office, 1947.
30. Leggett, William F. *Ancient and Medieval Dyes.* New York: Chemical Publishing Company, 1944.
31. Lewis, William. *Commercium Philosophico-Technicum.* London: Printed by H. Baldwin for the author, 1763.
32. Mackenzie, Colin. *Five Thousand Receipts in All the Useful and Domestic Arts.* Philadelphia: A. Small, 1825.
33. Mattioli, Pietro Andrea. *Commentaires . . . sur les six livres de ped. dioscoride.* Lyon: G. Roville, 1572.
34. Mettler, Cecilia C. *History of Medicine.* Philadelphia: The Blakiston Co., 1947.
35. Mitchell, Charles A., and Thomas C. Hepworth. *Inks, Their Composition and Manufacture.* 4th ed. London: C. Griffin & Co., 1937.
36. Moxon, Joseph. *Moxon's Mechanick Exercises.* 2 vols. 1683. Reprint. New York, The Typothetae of the City of New York, 1896.
37. Murray, Sir James A. H., ed. *A New English Dictionary on Historical Principles.* 10 vols. in 13. Oxford: The Clarendon Press, 1888–1928.
38. *New and Complete Dictionary of Arts and Sciences, Comprehending*

*All the Branches of Useful Knowledge, A.* By a society of gentlemen. 4 vols. London: W. Owen, 1754–55.
39. ——. 2d ed. 4 vols. 1763–64.
40. *New Family Receipt-Book, The.* New Haven: Howe & Spalding and Samuel Wadsworth, 1819.
41. *New General Dictionary of Arts and Sciences, A.* 3 vols. London: J. Cook, 1760?
42. *Painter's Companion; or, A Treatise on Colours, The.* Edited by G. Long. London: Printed by E. Rider for Robert Laurie and James Whittle, 1801.
43. *Penny Cyclopaedia of the Society for the Diffusion of Useful Kuowledge, The.* 27 vols. in 14. London: C. Knight, 1833–43.
44. Plinius Secundus, G. *The Natural History of Pliny.* 6 vols. London: H. G. Bohn, 1855–57.
45. "Receipt for Making Writing Ink, A." *Gentleman's Magazine,* XXIII (May, 1753), 212.
46. Robertson, Hannah. *The Young Ladies School of Arts.* 2 vols. in 1. Edinburgh: Robert Jameson, 1777.
47. [Ruscelli, Girolamo?] *The Secretes of the Reverende Mayster Alexis of Piemout.* London: John Kingstone for Nicolas Inglande, 1559.
48. Schmitt, Charles A. "The Chemistry of Writing Inks." *Journal of Chemical Education,* XXI (August, 1944), 413–14.
49. Schullian, Dorothy M. "Early Print Transfer." *Journal of the History of Medicine and Allied Sciences,* VII (Winter, 1952), 86–88.
50. Theophrastus. *Enquiry into Plants and Minor Works on Odors and Weather Signs.* 2 vols. New York: G. P. Putnam's Sons, 1916.
51. Thornton, T. C. *The Modern Cabinet of Arts.* London: J. S. Pratt, 1842.
52. Waters, Campbell E. *Inks.* U. S. National Bureau of Standards, Circular C426. Washington, D.C.: U.S. Government Printing Office, 1940.
53. Wattenbach, Wilhelm. *Das Schriftwesen im Mittelalter.* 2d ed., enlarged. Leipzig: S. Hirzel, 1875.
54. Weiss, Harry B. "The Writing Masters and Ink Manufacturers of New York City." *Bulletin of the New York Public Library,* LVI (August, 1952), 383–94.
55. Wright, Thomas. *Reliquiae Antiquae: Scraps from Ancient Manuscripts, Illustrating Chiefly Early English Literature and the English Language.* 2 vols. London, 1841–43.
56. Zimmerman, Elmer W., Charles G. Weber, and Arthur E. Kimberly. *Relation of Ink to the Preservation of Written Records.* U. S. National Bureau of Standards, Research Paper RP779. Washington, D.C.: U.S. Government Printing Office, 1935.

Paper

1. Barrow, William J. "The Barrow Method of Laminating Documents." *Journal of Documentary Reproduction,* II (June, 1939), 147–51.

2. ——. "An Evaluation of Document Restoration Processes." *American Documentation*, IV (April, 1953), 50–54.
3. ——. "Migration of Impurities in Paper." *Archivum*, III (1953).
4. ——. "Restoration Methods." *The American Archivist*, VI (July, 1943), 151–54.
5. Beckwith, Theodore Day, W. H. Swanson, and Thomas M. Iiams. *Deterioration of Paper: The Cause and Effect of Foxing*. Publications of the University of California at Los Angeles in Biological Sciences, vol. I, no. 13. Berkeley, Calif.: University of California Press, 1940.
6. Benjamin, Mary A. *Autographs: A Key to Collecting*. New York: R. R. Bowker Co., 1946.
7. Blanchet, Augustin. *Essai sur l'histoire du papier et de sa fabrication*. Pt. 1. Paris: E. Leroux, 1900.
8. Blum, André. *On the Origin of Paper*. Translated by Harry Miller Lydenberg. New York: R. R. Bowker Co., 1934.
9. Bolsée, J. "La restauration des documents aux Archives Générales du Royaume." *Archives, Bibliothèques, et Musées de Belgique*, XXI (1950), 3–10.
10. Braibant, Charles, ed. *Archives*. Numéro spécial de l'éducation nationale (1951), 33–35.
11. Braude, Felix. *Adhesives*. New York: Chemical Publishing Co., 1943.
12. Buchanan, Estelle D., and Robert Earle. *Bacteriology*. 4th ed. New York: The Macmillan Co., 1938.
13. Carson, Frederick T. *Effect of Humidity on Physical Properties of Paper*. U.S. National Bureau of Standards, Circular C445. Washington, D.C.: U.S. Government Printing Office, 1944.
14. Clapperton, Robert H. *Paper: An Historical Account of Its Making by Hand from the Earliest Times Down to the Present Day*. Oxford: Shakespeare Head Press, 1934.
15. Chakravorti, S. "A Review of the Lamination Process." *The Indian Archives*, I (October, 1947), 304–12.
16. Chambers, Ephraim. *Cyclopaedia; or An Universal Dictionary*. 2 vols. London: James and John Knapton, 1728.
17. *Cyclopedia; or, Universal Dictionary of Arts, Sciences, and Literature, The*. Edited by Abraham Rees. 41 vols. Philadelphia: S. F. Bradford, 1810–24.
18. Davis, Raymond. *Action of Charred Paper on the Photographic Plate and a Method of Deciphering Charred Records*. U. S. Bureau of Standards, Scientific Papers, no. 454. Washington, D.C.: U.S. Government Printing Office, 1922.
19. De Coetlogon, Dennis. *An Universal History of Arts and Sciences*. 2 vols. London: John Hart, 1741–45.
20. Diringer, David. *The Hand-Produced Book*. London: Hutchinson's Scientific and Technical Publications, 1953.
21. *Encyclopaedia Britannica*. 2d ed. 10 vols. Edinburgh: J. Balfour & Co., 1778–83.

22. *Encyclopedia Metropolitana.* Edited by Edward Smedley, Hugh James Rose, and Henry John Rose. 29 vols. London: B. Fellowes, 1845.
23. *Encyclopaedia; or, A Dictionary of Arts, Sciences, and Miscellaneous Literature.* 18 vols. Philadelphia: Thomas Dobson, 1790–97.
24. *Encyclopédie, ou dictionnaire raisonné des sciences, des arts, et des métiers.* Edited by Denis Diderot and Jean le Rond d'Alembert. 17 vols. Paris: Briasson, 1751–65. 2d ed. 36 vols. Geneva: Pellet, 1777–79.
25. Ellis, Roger. *The Principles of Archive Repair.* London: London School of Printing and Graphic Arts, 1951.
26. Evans, D. L. "The Lamination Process, a British View," British Records Association, Technical Section, *Bulletin* no. 18, (October, 1945), 10–14.
27. Evelyn, John. *The Diary of John Evelyn.* Edited by William Bray. 2 vols. London: J. M. Dent & Sons, 1911–12.
28. Falconer, William. *A General Dictionary of Arts and Sciences.* 2 vols. London: S. Crowder, 1765–66.
29. Fitzpatrick, John C. *Notes on the Care, Cataloging, Calendaring, and Arranging of Manuscripts.* 3d ed. U.S. Library of Congress, Division of Manuscripts. Washington, D.C.: U.S. Government Printing Office, 1928.
30. Gallo, Alfonso. "Il restauro mecconico Barrow." *Bolleltino del R. Instituto di Patologia del Libro,* X (1951), 119–26.
31. ——. *Patologia e terapia del libro.* Rome: Editrice Raggio, 1951.
32. Grant, Julius. *Books and Documents: Dating, Permanence and Preservation.* London: Grafton & Co., 1937.
33. Greathouse, Glen A., and Carl J. Wessel, eds. *Deterioration of Materials.* National Research Council, Prevention of Deterioration Center. New York: Reinhold Publishing Corp., 1954.
34. Hamilton, Robert M. "The Library of Parliament Fire." *The American Archivist,* XVI (April, 1953), 141–44.
35. Haselden, Reginald B. *Scientific Aids for the Study of Manuscripts.* Oxford: Oxford University Press for the Bibliographical Society, 1935.
36. Haynes, William. *Cellulose, the Chemical That Grows.* Garden City, N.Y.: Doubleday & Co., 1953.
37. Hunter, Dard. *Paper Making.* 2d ed. New York: Alfred A. Knopf, 1947.
38. ——. *Papermaking in Pioneer America.* Philadelphia: University of Pennsylvania Press, 1952.
39. Imberdis, Le P. Jean, S.J. *Papyrus, sive ars conficiendae papyri / Le papier, ou l'art de fabriquer le papier.* Translated by Augustin Blanchet. Paris: C. Beranger, 1899.
40. Imperial Record Department, New Delhi. *Notes on Preservation of Records.* Simla: Government of India Press, 1941.
41. Jarrell, T. D., J. M. Hankins, and F. P. Veitch. *Deterioration of Book and Record Papers.* U.S. Department of Agriculture, Technical Bulletin no. 541. Washington, D.C.: U.S. Government Printing Office, 1936.
42. Jenkinson, Sir Hiliary. *A Manual of Archive Administration.* Rev. ed. London: P. Lund, Humphries & Co., 1937.

43. ——. "The Principles and Practice of Archive Repair Work in England." *Archivum*, II (1952), 31–41.
44. Joint Textbook Committee of the Paper Industry of the United States and Canada. *The Manufacture of Pulp and Paper.* Vol. V. 3d ed. New York: McGraw-Hill Book Co., 1939.
45. Kantrowitz, Morris S., Ernest W. Spencer, and Robert H. Simmons. *Permanence and Durability of Paper, an Annotated Bibliography of the Technical Literature from 1885* A.D. *to 1939* A.D. U.S. Government Printing Office, Division of Tests and Technical Control, Technical Bulletin no. 22. Washington, D.C.: U.S. Government Printing Office, 1940.
46. Kimberly, Arthur E. "Repair and Preservation in the National Archives." *The American Archivist*, I (July, 1938), 111–17.
47. Kimberly, Arthur E., and Adelaide L. Emley. *A Study of the Deterioration of Book Papers in Libraries.* U.S. National Bureau of Standards, Miscellaneous Publication no. 140. Washington, D.C.: U.S. Government Printing Office, 1933.
48. [Knight, Charles.] *Knight's Cyclopaedia of the Industry of All Nations.* London, 1851.
49. [Koops, Matthias.] *Historical Account of the Substances Which Have Been Used to Describe Events, and to Convey Ideas, from the Earliest Date to the Invention of Paper.* London: T. Burton, 1800.
50. Kremer, Alvin W. "The Preservation of Wood Pulp Publications." *College and Research Libraries*, XV (April, 1954), 205–9.
51. Labarre, Emile Joseph. *Dictionary and Encyclopaedia of Paper and Paper-Making.* 2d ed., rev. Amsterdam: Swets & Zeitlinger, 1952.
52. Launer, Herbert F. *Determination of the pH Value of Papers.* U.S. National Bureau of Standards, Research Paper RP1205. Washington, D.C.: U.S. Government Printing Office, 1939.
53. Launer, Herbert F., and William K. Wilson. "The Photochemical Stability of Papers." *Paper Trade Journal*, CXVI (February 25, 1943), 28–36.
54. Le Gear, Clara Egli. *Maps: Their Care, Repair, and Preservation in Libraries.* U.S. Library of Congress, Division of Maps. Washington, D.C.: U.S. Government Printing Office, 1949.
55. Leggett, William F. *The Story of Linen.* New York: Chemical Publishing Co., 1945.
56. Lelande, Joseph Jérôme Le Français de. *Art de faire le papier.* Paris: Desaint et Saillant, 1761.
57. Lewis, Harry F. "Research for the Archivist of Today and Tomorrow." *The American Archivist*, XII (January, 1949), 9–17.
58. Lucas, Alfred. *Ancient Egyptian Materials and Industries.* 3d ed., rev. London: Edward Arnold & Co., 1948.
59. Minogue, Adelaide E. *The Repair and Preservation of Records.* National Archives Bulletin V. Washington, D.C.: U.S. Government Printing Office, 1943.

60. ——. "Treatment of Fire and Water Damaged Records." *The American Archivist*, IX (January, 1946), 17–25.
61. Munsell, Joel. *A Chronology of Paper and Paper-Making*. Albany: J. Munsell, 1857.
62. *New and Complete Dictionary of Arts and Sciences, Comprehending All the Branches of Useful Knowledge, A*. By a society of gentlemen. 4 vols. London: W. Owen, 1754–55. 2d ed. 4 vols. 1763–64.
63. Nixon, H. M. "Lamination of Paper Documents with Cellulose Acetate Foil." *Archives, the Journal of the British Records Association* (Michaelmas, 1949), 32–36.
64. Ott, Emil, ed. *Cellulose and Cellulose Derivatives*. New York: Interscience Publishers, 1946.
65. *Penny Cyclopaedia of the Society for the Diffusion of Useful Knowledge, The*. 27 vols. in 14. London: C. Knight, 1833–43.
66. Plenderleith, Harold J. *The Conservation of Prints, Drawings, and Manuscripts*. Oxford: Oxford University Press for the Museums Association, 1937.
67. *Preservation of the Declaration of Independence and the Constitution of the United States*. U.S. National Bureau of Standards, Circular 505. Washington, D.C.: U.S. Government Printing Office, 1951.
68. *Protective Display Lighting of Historical Documents*. U.S. National Bureau of Standards, Circular 538. Washington, D.C.: U.S. Government Printing Office, 1953.
69. "Restoration of an Ancient Manuscript." *The Library of Congress Quarterly Journal*, X (November, 1952), 13–17.
70. Richter, George A. "Relative Permanence of Papers Exposed to Sunlight." *Industrial and Engineering Chemistry*, XXVII (February, April, 1935), 177–85, 432–39.
71. Schullian, Dorothy M. "Early Print Transfer." *Journal of the History of Medicine and Allied Sciences*, VII (Winter, 1952), 86–88.
72. Scribner, B. W. *Comparison of Accelerated Aging of Record Papers with Normal Aging for Eight Years*. U.S. National Bureau of Standards, Research Paper RP1241. Washington, D.C.: U.S. Government Printing Office, 1939.
73. ——. *Protection of Documents with Cellulose Acetate Sheeting*. U.S. National Bureau of Standards, Miscellaneous Publication M168. Washington, D.C.: U.S. Government Printing Office, 1940.
74. *Select Essays: Containing the Manner of Raising and Dressing Flax and Hemp, also the Whole Method of Bleaching or Whitening Linen-Cloth*. Philadelphia: Robert Bell, 1777.
75. Shaw, Merle B., George W. Bicking, and Martin J. O'Leary. *A Study of the Relation of Some Properties of Cotton Rags to the Strength and Stability of Experimental Papers Made from Them*. U.S. National Bureau of Standards, Research Paper RP794. Washington, D.C.: U.S. Government Printing Office, 1935.

76. Shaw, Merle B., and Martin J. O'Leary. *Effect of Filling and Sizing Materials on Stability of Book Papers.* U.S. National Bureau of Standards, Research Paper RP1149. Washington, D.C.: U.S. Government Printing Office, 1938.
77. Siu, Ralph G. H. *Microbial Decomposition of Cellulose, with Special Reference to Cotton Textiles.* New York: Reinhold Publishing Corp., 1951.
78. Smith, L. Herman. "Manuscript Repair in European Archives." *The American Archivist,* I (January–April, 1938), 1–22, 51–77.
79. Still, John S. "Library Fire and Salvage Methods." *The American Archivist,* XVI (April, 1953), 145–53.
80. Technical Association of the Pulp and Paper Industry. *Pulpwood Stands: Procurement and Utilization.* TAPPI Monograph Series, no. 4. New York: The Association, 1947.
81. Tollenaar, D. "L'acetate de cellulose et la lamination des documents." *Archivum,* II (1952), 51–53.
82. Tribolet, Harold W. "Binding and Related Problems." *The American Archivist,* XVI (April, 1953), 115–26.
83. Torrey, W. V., and E. Sutermeister. "A Brief Study of Some Old Papers." *Paper Trade Journal,* XCVI (May 25, 1933), 45–46.
84. Van Schreeven, William J. "The Filing Arrangement of the Archives Division, Virginia State Library." *American Archivist,* XI (July, 1948), 248–51.
85. Weeks, Lyman Horace. *A History of Paper Manufacturing in the United States, 1690–1916.* New York: The Lockwood Trade Journal Co., 1916.